15·00

Project
Specification

What is this Code about?

Under all forms of building contract the proposed work needs to be described comprehensively yet concisely. Such description may appear as a specification, as notes on the drawings, as a schedule of work, or as preambles or headings to bills of quantities. This Code is concerned mainly with full specifications or 'specification preambles'.

Who is the Code for?

The Code is for use by all members of the design team. It applies equally to the building fabric and building services.

Why is the Code needed?

There is much evidence that specification can and should be improved so that it is comprehensive, appropriate, accurate and up to date, thus providing a definitive basis for quality. Although excellent libraries of specification clauses exist, there is at present no industry document which concisely and authoritatively sets down the underlying principles of specification. This Code seeks to fill that gap.

Co-ordination of project documents.

In addition to being technically sound, specifications need to be well co-ordinated with drawings and bills of quantities. This Code gives recommendations on how this can be achieved, including use of CCPI's Common Arrangement of Work Sections (CAWS).

Relationship with the Code for Production Drawings.

The Code of Procedure for Production Drawings, also produced under the auspices of CCPI, is intended to be used in conjunction with this Code. The two documents cover, respectively, the graphic and descriptive information produced by designers for use by builders. They have been written with a view to improving drawings and specifications, and the co-ordination between them.

Relationship with SMM7 and the Code for Bills of Quantities.

The Code of Procedure for Bills of Quantities, published in conjunction with SMM7, recommends that project bills and specifications are arranged in accordance with CAWS. Part B of this Code for Project Specification provides detailed guidance on coverage of project preliminaries, specifications and specification preambles which will, inter alia, help users to meet the requirements of SMM7.

What backing does the Code have?

The development of the Code was overseen by the Co-ordinating Committee for Project Information. It was drafted by a Specification Working Group (see Appendix 1) set up by CCPI's four sponsoring bodies, the Association of Consulting Engineers, Building Employer's Confederation, Royal Institute of British Architects and Royal Institution of Chartered Surveyors, who have formally approved the Code and recommend its use.

Project Specification

A code of procedure for building works

Co-ordinated project information

First edition, December 1987

Published by the Building Project Information Committee

Copyright
© 1987

Association of Consulting Engineers
Building Employers Confederation
Royal Institute of British Architects
The Royal Institution of Chartered Surveyors

ISBN 0 9512662 2 5

Set and printed by NBS Services Ltd, Newcastle upon Tyne

Contents

Foreword   1

Part A General principles

1 Nature and purpose of specification information   4
   1.1 What is specification information?
   1.2 What is a project specification?
   1.3 What does a project specification contain?
   1.4 What is a project specification for?

2 Background and objectives   6
   2.1 Historical background
   2.2 Recent trends
   2.3 The need to improve standards

3 Co-ordination of specification with drawings, quantities and schedules   8
   3.1 The 'Common arrangement of work sections'
   3.2 Where should specification information be given?
   3.3 Annotation of drawings (with example)
   3.4 Measured item descriptions (with example)
   3.5 Example specification section
   3.6 Co-ordination on smaller projects

4 Specification techniques   20
   4.1 Specification by performance or prescription
   4.2 Specification of options and alternatives
   4.3 Specification by reference or description
   4.4 How to specify by reference

5 What should be specified?   25
   5.1 General
   5.2 Standard products and materials
   5.3 Purpose made components and assemblies
   5.4 Workmanship
   5.5 When the specification needs to be brief

6 Arrangement and presentation of the specification   29
   6.1 Arrangement of the specification into work sections
   6.2 Arrangement within the work sections
   6.3 Language of specifications

7 Producing the specification   33
   7.1 Who should prepare the specification?
   7.2 The need for knowledge and information
   7.3 Libraries of clauses
   7.4 A model procedure
   7.5 Presentation of the specification

Part B Guidance on coverage

A Preliminaries/General conditions   40

   A10 Project particulars
   A11 Drawings
   A12 The site/Existing buildings
   A13 Description of the work
   A20 The Contract/Sub-contract
   A30 Employer's requirements:
         Tendering/Sub-letting/Supply
   A31 Employer's requirements:
         Provision, content and use of documents
   A32 Employer's requirements:
         Management of the Works
   A33 Employer's requirements:
         Quality standards/control
   A34 Employer's requirements:
         Security/Safety/Protection
   A35 Employer's requirements:
         Specific limitations on method/sequence/timing
   A36 Employer's requirements:
         Facilities/Temporary works/Services
   A37 Employer's requirements:
         Operation/Maintenance of the finished building
   A40 Contractor's general cost items:
         Management and staff
   A41 Contractor's general cost items:
         Site accommodation
   A42 Contractor's general cost items:
         Services and facilities
   A43 Contractor's general cost items:
         Mechanical plant
   A44 Contractor's general cost items:
         Temporary works
   A50 Work/Materials by the Employer
   A51 Nominated sub-contractors
   A52 Nominated suppliers
   A53 Work by statutory authorities
   A54 Provisonal work
   A55 Dayworks

B Complete buildings

   Checklists not included

C Demolition/Alteration/Renovation   45

   C41 Chemical dpcs to existing walls
   C52 Fungus/Beetle eradication

D Groundwork   46

   D20 Excavating and filling

E In situ concrete/Large precast concrete 47

E10 In situ concrete
E20 Formwork for in situ concrete
E30 Reinforcement for in situ concrete
E40 Designed joints in in situ concrete
E41 Worked finishes/Cutting to in situ concrete
E50 Precast concrete large units

F Masonry 50

F10 Brick/Block walling
F20 Natural stone rubble walling
F21 Natural stone/ashlar walling/dressings
F30 Accessories/Sundry items for brick/block/stone walling
F31 Precast concrete sills/lintels/copings/features

G Structural/Carcassing metal/timber 52

G10 Structural steel framing
G20 Carpentry/Timber framing/First fixing

H Cladding/Covering 54

H10 Patent glazing
H13 Structural glass assemblies
H21 Timber weatherboarding
H30 Fibre cement profiled sheet cladding/covering/siding
H31 Metal profiled/flat sheet cladding/covering/siding
H41 Glass reinforced plastics cladding/features
H50 Precast concrete slab cladding/features
H51 Natural stone slab cladding/features
H52 Cast stone slab cladding/features
H60 Clay/Concrete roof tiling
H61 Fibre cement slating
H62 Natural slating
H71 Lead sheet coverings/flashings

J Waterproofing 60

J20 Mastic asphalt tanking/damp proof membranes
J21 Mastic asphalt roofing/insulation/finishes
J30 Liquid applied tanking/damp proof membranes
J40 Flexible sheet tanking/damp proof membranes
J41 Built up felt roof coverings

K Linings/Sheathing/Dry partitioning 63

K10 Plasterboard dry lining
K11 Rigid sheet flooring/sheathing/linings/casings
K12 Under purlin/Inside rail panel linings
K13 Rigid sheet fine linings/panelling
K20 Timber board flooring/sheathing/linings/casings
K21 Timber narrow strip flooring/linings
K31 Plasterboard fixed partitions/inner walls/linings
K40 Suspended ceilings

L Windows/Doors/Stairs   66
L10, L11, L12 Windows/Rooflights/Screens/Louvres
L20, L21, L22 Doors/Shutters/Hatches
L30, L31 Stairs/Walkways/Balustrades
L40 General glazing

M Surface finishes   69
M10 Sand cement/Concrete/Granolithic screeds/flooring
M11 Mastic asphalt flooring
M20 Plastered/Rendered/Roughcast coatings
M30 Metal mesh lathing/Anchored reinforcement for plastered coatings
M40 Stone/Concrete/Quarry/Ceramic tiling/Mosaic
M41 Terrazzo tiling/In situ terrazzo
M50 Rubber/Plastics/Cork/Lino/Carpet tiling/sheeting
M51 Edge fixed carpeting
M52 Decorative papers/fabrics
M60 Painting/Clear finishing

N Furniture/Equipment   74
N13 Sanitary appliances/fittings

P Building fabric sundries   75
P10 Sundry insulation/proofing work/fire stops
P11 Foamed/Fibre/Bead cavity wall insulation
P20 Unframed isolated trims/skirtings/sundry items
P30 Trenches/Pipeways/Pits for buried engineering services
P31 Holes/Chases/Covers/Supports for services

Q Paving/Planting/Fencing/Site furniture   77
Q10 Stone/Concrete/Brick kerbs/edgings/channels
Q20 Hardcore/Granular/Cement bound bases/sub-bases to roads/pavings
Q22 Coated macadam/Asphalt roads/pavings
Q24 Interlocking brick/block roads/pavings
Q25 Slab/Brick/Sett/Cobble pavings
Q30 Seeding/Turfing
Q31 Planting
Q40 Fencing
Q50 Site/Street furniture/equipment

R Disposal systems   81
R10 Rainwater pipework/gutters
R11 Foul drainage above ground
R12 Drainage below ground
R13 Land drainage
R20 Sewage pumping

S Piped supply systems   83

S10 Cold water
S11 Hot water
S12 Hot and cold water (small scale)
S13 Pressurised water
S21 Swimming pool water treatment
S41 Fuel oil storage/distribution
S60 Fire hose reels
S61 Dry risers
S62 Wet risers
S63 Sprinklers

T Mechanical heating/Cooling/Refrigeration systems   87

T10 Gas/Oil fired boilers
T11 Coal fired boilers
T12 Electrode/Direct electric boilers
T13 Packaged steam generators
T20 Primary heat distribution
T30 Medium temperature hot water heating
T31 Low temperature hot water heating
T32 Low temperature hot water heating (small scale)
T40 Warm air heating
T60 Central refrigeration plant
T61 Primary/Secondary cooling distribution

U Ventilation/Air conditioning systems   92

U10 General supply/extract
U11 Toilet extract
U12 Kitchen extract
U31 VAV air conditioning
U32 Dual-duct air conditioning
U40 Induction air conditioning
U41 Fan-coil air conditioning
U42 Terminal re-heat air conditioning

V Electrical supply/Power/Lighting systems   95

V12 LV supply/public utility supply
V20 LV distribution
V21 General lighting
V40 Emergency lighting
V90 General lighting and power (small scale)

W Communications/Security/Control systems   97

W50 Fire detection and alarm
W51 Earthing and bonding
W52 Lightning protection
W61 Central control

X Transport systems

Checklists not included

Y Services reference specification   99

Y10   Pipelines
Y11   Pipeline ancillaries
Y20   Pumps
Y21   Water tanks/cisterns
Y22   Heat exchangers
Y23   Storage cylinders/calorifiers
Y24   Trace heating
Y25   Cleaning and chemical treatment
Y30   Air ductlines
Y31   Air ductline ancillaries
Y40   Air handling units
Y41   Fans
Y42   Air filtration
Y43   Heating/Cooling coils
Y44   Humidifiers
Y45   Silencers/Acoustic treatment
Y46   Grilles/Diffusers/Louvres
Y50   Thermal insulation
Y51   Testing and commissioning of mechanical services
Y52   Vibration isolation mountings
Y53   Control components – mechanical
Y54   Identification – mechanical
Y60   Conduit and cable trunking
Y61   HV/LV cables and wiring
Y62   Busbar trunking
Y63   Support components – cables
Y71   LV switchgear and distribution boards
Y72   Contactors and starters
Y73   Luminaires and lamps
Y74   Accessories for electrical services
Y80   Earthing and bonding components
Y81   Testing and commissioning of electrical services
Y82   Identification – electrical
Y90   Fixing to building fabric
Y91   Off-site painting/Anti-corrosion treatments
Y92   Motor drives – electric

Z Building fabric reference specification   112

Z10   Purpose made joinery
Z11   Purpose made metalwork
Z20   Fixings/Adhesives
Z21   Mortars
Z22   Sealants
Z30   Off-site painting

Part C Libraries of clauses

National Building Specification   116
National Engineering Specification   122

Appendix 1

Members of the Specification Working   131
Group and Consultant

Abbreviations

ACE	Association of Consulting Engineers
BEC	Building Employers Confederation
BRE	Building Research Establishment
BS	British Standard
BSI	British Standards Institution
CA	Contract Administrator
CAWS	Common arrangement of work sections for building works
CCPI	Co-ordinating Committee for Project Information
CP	British Standard Code of Practice
JCT	Joint Contracts Tribunal
NBS	National Building Specification
NCC	National Consultative Council
NES	National Engineering Specification
PIG	Project Information Group of the NCC Standing Committee
PSA	Property Services Agency
QSRMC	Quality Scheme for Ready Mixed Concrete
RIBA	Royal Institute of British Architects
RICS	Royal Institution of Chartered Surveyors
SMM	Standard Method of Measurement of Building Works
WOBS	BS 8000 'Workmanship on building sites'

Foreword

The Co-ordinated Project Information Initiative

It has long been appreciated that when the information provided to contractors is insufficient, conflicting or incorrect, this leads to problems on site with a consequent reduction in the quality of the work, delays and increased costs. The government sponsored Project Information Group (PIG) identified the trends and difficulties in 1979 and recommended the action which should be taken to effect an improvement. The Co-ordinated Project Information (CPI) initiative by the Industry followed; to extend, clarify and simplify the national conventions used in communication between designers and contractors. The initiative has been sponsored by ACE, BEC (formerly NFBTE), RIBA and RICS and represents a unique working together of builders, architects, quantity surveyors, structural and services engineers over a period of over six years. Annual approval has been obtained from the four Institutions to advance, stage by stage and the final documents have taken into account the many comments received following publication of drafts in 1984.

Financial support has come from the Department of the Environment in the form of commissioned studies, effort in kind by BRE and support for the launch of CPI. Further finance has come from the four Sponsoring Bodies for the administration of the operation and more commissioned studies, but the majority of the effort has been on a voluntary basis by representatives of the four disciplines.

The Co-ordinating Committee for Project Information, having now completed its work, is confident that if the conventions are followed they will contribute to better planned projects leading to more expeditious construction at lower cost and with better quality control. The potential for improved performance will, however, be dependent upon the willingness of those who commission buildings to allow the deployment of adequate resources at the design stage for the preparation of the necessary full and properly co-ordinated documentation.

I am glad to have this opportunity to express my thanks to all those who have so willingly contributed their time and experience towards the completion of this major initiative.

24 April 1987

Alex Gordon
Chairman, CCPI

Part A
General principles

1 Nature and purpose of specification information

1.1 What is specification?

Specification can be thought of as a process, a type of written information or a type of document. As a process it is an inherent part of design, and consists of determining and communicating the nature and quality of each element, system, assembly, component, material and item of workmanship. Specification information is the written description resulting from the specification process, and may be included in virtually any type of document, e.g. drawings, schedules, project specifications and bills of quantities.

Specification information is used at all stages of design and construction, whenever there is a need for one party to inform another of its requirements and whenever there is a need to make a formal record of an agreement or decision, e.g.

- The client's brief may include particular performance requirements or preferences for certain materials or components.
- Financial analysis statements or cost plans need to state the materials, systems and other assumptions allowed for under each elemental category.
- Design drawings and reports for presentation to the client need to confirm the main materials, methods of construction and building services systems being proposed.
- Submissions for statutory approvals need to define the proposed construction, particularly in relation to appearance, health and safety.
- The contract documents define the quality of the work which the contractor is required to provide.
- Instructions issued to the contractor during the course of the Works give additional specification information to clarify or, in some cases, to vary the requirements stated in the contract documents.

1.2 What is a project specification?

Definition

Whilst specification information exists at many stages in the development of a building project, this Code of Procedure is concerned with the specification information included in contract documents. In this context 'the project specification' is defined as *'a document or part of a document, the main purpose of which is to define the materials and products to be used, the standard of work required, any performance requirements, and the conditions under which the work is to be executed.'*

JCT with quantities contracts

Under many standard forms of contract the project specification is a contract document in its own right, but under the Joint Contracts Tribunal 'With Quantities' forms it is not. Under such contracts it has been normal practice to include specification information as 'preambles' to the bills of quantities. The term 'preambles' has no particular significance (it does not appear in the JCT forms) and 'specification' is therefore recommended as a preferred term. Whichever term is used, it is important that the specification text is given the status of a Contract Document by incorporating it into the Contract Bills – this can be done by clearly titling it, e.g. 'Bill number 2: Specification'. Alternatively, it may be divided up as specification preambles to the various sections of measured work.

Schedules of work

Similarly, on 'Without Quantities' projects, the terms 'specification' and 'schedule' (or 'schedule of work') have often been confused. A schedule of work is a list of the various items of work to be done, normally to an existing building, and usually set out on a locational or room by room basis. It is usually used as a pricing document on 'Without Quantities' contracts and as such can be considered as a substitute for:

- A bill of quantities, although in general measured quantities are not included. In order to determine the quantities and circumstances for each item of work it is usually necessary for the estimator to inspect the existing building and/or refer to drawings. Quantities are sometimes given, e.g. for provisional items.
- Heavily annotated drawings, which would otherwise be used as the basis for a lump sum price.

A schedule of work, as described above, has often been referred to as a 'specification' but this is unhelpful: it is recommended that such documents are titled 'Schedule of work'. A specification will usually be required in addition to the schedule of work.

Pricing documents

It will be seen from the definition and discussion above that the specification is not a pricing document, but rather a document giving qualitative information in support of the pricing document, which may be either measured quantities, drawings, or a schedule of work.

1.3 What does a project specification contain?

The project specification comprises requirements:

- relating to the works as a whole (Preliminaries) in respect of the form of contract, tendering, provision and use of documents, control of the works, temporary works and services, etc.
- that products and materials must be of a particular type or standard;
- that work operations of various kinds must be carried out in a certain way or to give a stated result;
- that the completed work must have certain characteristics and properties;
- that certain procedures must be followed in respect of such things as sub-contracting, detailing, approvals, testing and completion of the work.

1.4 What is a project specification for?

The purpose of a project specification, in conjunction with drawn, scheduled and measured information, is to define the quality of the systems, components, materials, workmanship and the finished work in such a way that the employer, contractor and professional advisers can have a reasonable degree of certainty that:

- the designer's detailed requirements will be met, compliance being judged on a definitive basis;
- the contractor's estimator can price the work with certainty and accuracy;
- the contractor can order materials and components correctly and in good time;
- the contractor can plan, execute and supervise the work in a controlled manner;
- the contract will be brought to a successful conclusion with the minimum number of misundertandings and variations.

2 Background and objectives

2.1 Historical background

It is widely recognised that standards of specification writing have been, in general, much lower than they should. With certain significant exceptions normal practice has been as follows:

Architectural specifications

On projects with quantities architects have not, in general, prepared a formal specification even though it is their responsibility. The task has normally been left to the quantity surveyor as part of the production of bills of quantities (A). Quantity surveyors, not being the designers, are not in a position to determine specification information with certainty and precision. The result has been that 'architectural' specification, produced as preambles to bills of quantities, has tended to be inadequate in coverage, over-generalised, often out of date and not very useful.

On projects without quantities the production of the specification is governed by a different set of circumstances. Because fee scales have been based on a percentage of total cost of the works, designers of small jobs have had a strictly limited amount of time to spend on specification, even though the work may need to be to a high quality standard. Designers have also been concerned that tender documents should not seem to be too onerous to the builder, in case this has an inflationary effect on tender prices. Specification on small, without quantities projects has therefore tended to suffer the same faults as in with quantities practice, comprising just a few generalised clauses to support the drawings and/or schedules of work.

Structural engineering specifications

These, especially for concrete work, have tended to be very thorough and long. They sometimes require unreasonably high standards of work or are unnecessarily restrictive but the most obvious shortcoming is their needless variety in technical content and presentation. In common with other professional groups, structural engineers have difficulty in ensuring that their specifications reflect the most up to date industry documents and procedures.

Mechanical and electrical engineering specifications

These have tended to be kept separate from the building fabric specification by the almost universal practice of nomination of specialist sub-contractors. The normal Conditions of Engagement for services consultants have not included detailed design, this being carried out, at least in part, by the services sub-contractors. The tender documents have thus normally been a schematic set of drawings supported by a specification including both performance requirements and quality of materials and workmanship. The specifications are usually bulky, perhaps excessively so, and also suffer from needless variety from one design office to another.

2.2 Recent trends

Against the general background of traditional practice a number of more recent developments and trends can be discerned:

- Concern in the industry about the effect which poor and uncertain project information has on the efficiency of construction work (B).

- An increasing consciousness of differences between the construction industries of the UK and other countries, particularly the USA. One of the major differences to be noted is that in other countries the specification plays a much more important and useful role than in the UK.
- A general concern in the industry at the high level of claims for additional cost, it being realised that a large proportion of claims are generated by lack of certainty and accuracy in the project documents.
- The research work carried out by the Building Research Establishment (C) which has shown a disturbingly high incidence of defects which become apparent during construction, over 50% of these being due to inadequate design and specification.
- The proposals for SMM7, which emphasise the need for adequate drawn and specified information.
- The development of the National Building Specification and its use by an increasing number of practitioners, particularly architects, to produce detailed project specifications.
- The development of the National Engineering Specification for M and E Services to operate in a manner similar to NBS.
- The development of BS 8000: 'Workmanship on building sites' (D) in order to define basic good practice in workmanship for more common kinds of building work.

2.3 The need to improve standards

The purpose of this Code is to assist in remedying the deficiencies of practice described at 2.1 and to respond to the concerns and reinforce the trends described at 2.2. Significant improvement is sought so that project specifications are:

- Comprehensive, covering every significant aspect of quality.
- Produced specifically for each project, with no irrelevant material.
- Appropriate, requirements being specified having regard to the nature of the project and the available knowledge, resources and means of verification.
- Practicable, requirements being specified only if this can be demonstrated. Once specified, requirements should be enforced.
- Constructive, in other words helpfully specific, so that all parties know what is expected of them.
- Up to date, reflecting current good building practice and the most recent published industry standards.
- Clearly and economically worded – the objective is to transfer information from designers to builders with speed and certainty.
- Arranged in accordance with the 'Common arrangement of work sections' (E) and the recommendations for arrangement of information within work sections given in part 6.5 of this Code.
- Standardised – needless variety in technical content and presentation should be reduced by sensible use of high quality libraries of specification clauses.

(A) 'The Selection and Specification of Building Materials and Components', Institute of Advanced Architectural Studies, Research Paper 17, May 1980.
(B) Report of NCC Project Information Group, 1979.
(C) BRE Current Paper 7/81 "Quality Control on Building Sites"
   BRE Report 'Quality in traditional housing, Volume 1: an investigation into faults and their avoidance' 1982.
   'Achievement of quality on building sites' NEDO 1987.
(D) Publication expected 1988.
(E) 'Common arrangement of work sections for building works' BPIC 1987.

3 Co-ordination of specification with drawings, quantities and schedules

3.1 The 'Common arrangement of work sections'

Co-ordination involves ensuring that:

- the information given in a document does not conflict with information given elsewhere;
- the various project documents, when read together, give all the necessary information;
- the parts of the documents which relate to each other are identified precisely and can be found easily.

The Common arrangement of work sections (CAWS) has been developed by CCPI to facilitate the last of these requirements and is recommended for the arrangement of project specifications, preambles and measured quantities.

CAWS is designed to replace the traditional arrangements of specifications and bills of quantities, which usually have consisted of 15–20 'trade' sections. The division of information for sub-contracting is usually much finer than this so that the contractor has unnecessary work in dividing up and editing the project information. A set of common categories at this finer level should make it easier to divide information for distribution to sub-contractors and suppliers both for estimating and subsequently getting the work built.

CAWS includes about 300 work sections, derived from close observation of the pattern of sub-contracting in the industry. The sections vary widely in their scope and nature, reflecting the large range of building materials, products, specialists and sub-contractors which now exist.

A detailed definition is given for each CA work section in order that project documents can be more consistent in their arrangement and to help ensure that gaps and overlaps between sections do not occur. Three example definitions are given on page 9; reference should be made to the full set of definitions given in the CAWS publication.

The arrangement is set out in three levels, the third and lowest of these being the work sections. The three levels have been given the following titles:

Level 1 – Group   e.g. D   Groundwork
Level 2 – Sub-group   e.g. D3   Piling
Level 3 – Work Sections e.g. D30   Cast in place concrete piling.

It is anticipated that project specifications and bills of quantities will use Level 1 (Group) and Level 3 (Work Section) headings and codes, but not Level 2 (Sub-group). Part B of this Code is arranged by CAWS and uses only Level 1 and 3 headings and codes.

An important feature of CAWS, particularly for mechanical and electrical

D30
Cast in place concrete piling

All forms of bored in situ concrete piling including driven shell piles where the shell is withdrawn and the pile formed with in situ concrete.

Included

Boring and enlarging bases
Driving and withdrawing shells
In situ concrete
Reinforcement
Disposing of excavated material
Testing

Excluded

Preformed concrete piling, D31
Driven precast concrete shell piling where the shell is not withdrawn
(Preformed concrete piling, D31)
Pile caps and ground beams
(Relevant sections)
Breaking out concrete to tops of piles and preparing pile heads and reinforcement for capping
(In situ concrete, E10)

H10
Patent glazing

Glass sheets set into independent metal glazing bars fixed to structural supports to form glazed roofs, walls, lantern lights, skylights, etc.

Included

Glazing bars of galvanized, lead sheathed, or plastics sheathed steel, or of aluminium, with integral lead or aluminium wings and/or plastics or aluminium cappings including fixing
Rough cast, wired rough cast, float, wired ground and polished and other single and double glazing
Opening portions, including frames and opening gear
Ventilators, including opening and control gear
Fixing shoes, glass stops, weather bars, etc.
Raking and curved cutting
Glazing compounds, tapes, beads, distance pieces, etc.
Flashings and weatherproofing of adjoining work when executed as part of the patent glazing

Excluded

Curtain walling, H11
Plastics glazed vaulting/walling, H12
Structural glass assemblies, H13
Malleable sheet flashings when not executed as part of the patent glazing
(Relevant section, H71–H76)
Drilling metalwork, etc. for fixing patent glazing
(Relevant section)

U40
Induction air conditioning

An air conditioning system serving a variety of perimeter spaces with limited depth, control being effected by the minimal primary air supply being squirted through nozzles in the induction unit, inducing room air to pass over heating and cooling coils to adjust the final temperature. The induction units are supplied with water from the plantroom by 2, 3 or 4 pipe systems for temperature control purposes. The system has minimal supply and extract from the plantroom. Distribution is usually at medium or high pressure.

Included
Reference specification items

Pipelines, Y10
Pipeline ancillaries, Y11
Pumps, Y20
Cleaning and chemical treatment, Y25
Air ductlines, Y30
Air ductline ancillaries, Y31
Air handling units, Y40
Fans, Y41
Air filtration, Y42
Heating/Cooling coils, Y43
Humidifiers, Y44
Silencers/Acoustic treatment, Y45
Grilles/Diffusers/Louvres, Y46
Thermal insulation, Y50
Testing and commissioning of mechanical services, Y51.
Vibration isolation mountings, Y52
Control components – mechanical, Y53
Identification – mechanical, Y54
Sundry common mechanical items, Y59
Contactors and starters, Y72
Fixing to building fabric, Y90
Off site painting and anti-corrosion treatments, Y91
Motor drives – electric, Y92

Particular specification items

Induction units

Excluded

Ventilated ceilings, K40
Heat source
(Various sections, T1)
Refrigeration plant and cooling towers
(Central refrigeration, T60)
LV distribution, V20
Central control, W61
Builder's work including on-site painting
(Various sections)

services, is the structuring into 'system' sections, e.g. 'Low temperature hot water heating' and 'reference specification' sections, e.g. 'Pipelines' and 'Pumps'. A project may include several 'systems' sections, each of which can then refer, as appropriate, to the 'reference specification' sections in order to avoid repetition. Reference specification sections are also used for some common aspects of building fabric specification, e.g. Mortar.

Obviously it is necessary for CAWS to include all types of work in common use in the UK. This, together with the 'narrow scope' approach adopted has resulted in a considerable increase in the number of work sections compared with traditional practice. However it will be found that only 10–30% of the sections will apply to one project.

3.2 Where should specification information be given?

Specification information can be given in several places – in a project specification, on drawings, in bills of quantities or in various types of schedule. Careful thought should be given to the way in which this is done, the following points being pertinent:

- Convenience of use:
  Locating part of the specification information for a given type of work in the project specification and part in another document (e.g. the measured quantities) can be inconvenient. For most purposes, e.g. ordering of materials or quality control on site, having the complete specification for each type of work in one place will be far more convenient.
- First point of reference:
  It is important that project documents are reasonably consistent and predictable in their arrangement. The project specification is concerned with the types and qualities of materials and work, and when questions about quality arise the first point of reference should be the project specification. The practice of spreading specification information among several documents, e.g. drawings, quantities, schedules and project specification can result in parts of it being overlooked.
- Ensuring use of the project specification:
  If substantial but incomplete specification information is given on the drawings or in the quantities or schedules, the contractor may be tempted to proceed without checking the specification. This danger will be reduced if relatively short 'identification' descriptions and cross references to the specification are given.
- Discrepancies and divergences:
  If substantial specification information is given on the drawings or in the quantities and/or schedules, the danger of discrepancies and divergences will be increased. The same thing may be described in the specification, on say four drawings and in three places in the quantities. The danger will be much reduced if the descriptions on the drawings and in the quantities are kept short. Also, avoidance of repetition will help to keep the quantities brief and avoid the drawings becoming crowded with information.
- Pre-contract procedures:
  The inclusion of substantial specification on drawings and in quantities and schedules can have an important effect on pre-contract procedures. If the descriptions are to be long, it is necessary to finalise the specification in detail at an early date. On the other hand if the descriptions are to be brief, annotation of the drawings and preparation of the measured item descriptions can proceed on the basis of an outline specification. The full specification can then be prepared while the other documents are being finalised. With a tight pre-contract programme, the difference can be important.

Therefore it is recommended that full specification information is normally given only in the project specification. Greater predictability and freedom from discrepancy will usually result if drawings, quantities and schedules *identify* the different kinds and qualities of work, but do not aim to *specify* them. This can be achieved by using a few carefully chosen words with, as appropriate, a reference to the relevant part of the specification. Such disciplined separation of graphic, scheduled, measured and specification information assumes and depends on the documents being arranged and cross-referenced in a way which makes it easy to read them together. An example of such co-ordination, based on use of CAWS, is given in the following sections:

3.3 Annotation of drawings
3.4 Measured item descriptions
3.5 Example specification section

3.3 Annotation of drawings

Specification information should not be put on a drawing simply because the designer has it to hand. It should be put on only for good reason, either because the drawing has specifically been produced to give that information, or because it provides essential 'context'. More extensive guidance is given in the Code for Production Drawings.

The example given below has been produced specifically to illustrate specification referencing of drawings; it does not purport to be complete – in particular information on setting out, levels and external paving is incomplete. The references, e.g. R12/101 can be looked up in the project specification given in section 3.5.

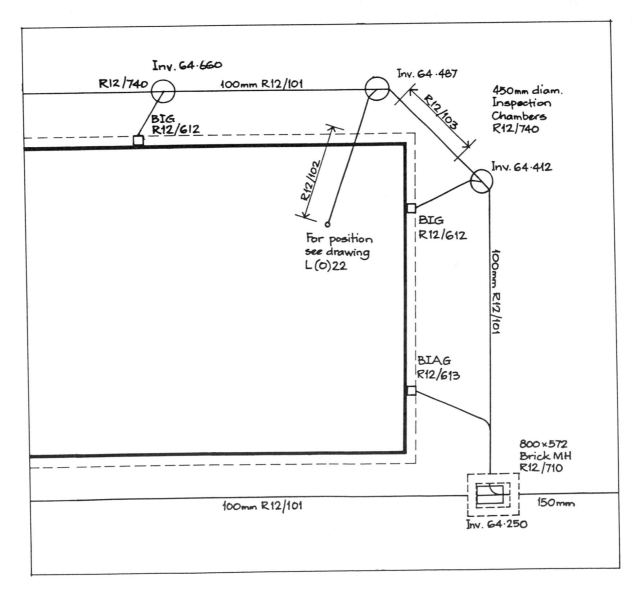

3.4 Measured item descriptions

The SMM7 General Rules provide that descriptive information *'may be given in documents (e.g. drawings and specification) separate from the bills of quantities if a precise and unique cross reference is given in its place in the description of the item concerned'*. Thus SMM7 is linked to the recommendation in 3.3 above that full specification is normally given only in the project specification, the drawings and quantities identifying the various kinds and qualities of work by a few carefully chosen words with, as appropriate, a reference to the relevant clause(s) in the specification. Thus in the example given below the 'Spec' references can be looked up in the project specification given in 3.5.

Whilst SMM7 requires the provision of adequate specification, it does not define this in detail. The test is that the designers' requirements are met and that there will be no contractor's claims based on inadequate specification. The specification check-lists included in Part B of this Code will help practitioners ensure that relevant specification information is not overlooked.

	R	DISPOSAL SYSTEMS				R
		R12 DRAINAGE BELOW GROUND				
		<u>Excavating trenches</u>				
		For pipes				
	A	Not exceeding 200 mm nominal size; 0.75 m average depth	35 m			
	B	Not exceeding 200 mm nominal size; 1.00 m average depth	144 m			
	C	Not exceeding 200 mm nominal size; 1.25 m average depth	30 m			
		<u>Disposal</u>				
	D	Surface water	Item			
		<u>Class D natural bed and selected fill surround Spec 340</u>				
		For pipes				
	E	100 mm nominal size; 400 x 250 mm thick	147 m			
	F	150 mm nominal size; 450 x 300 mm thick	35 m			
		<u>Class X concrete bed and surround Spec 350-480</u>				
		For pipes				
	G	100 mm nominal size; 400 x 400 mm thick	30 m			
	H	100 mm nominal size; 400 x 750 mm thick	7 m			
		<u>Vitrified clay pipework Spec 101-103</u>				
	J	100 mm nominal size; in trench	174 m			
	K	150 mm nominal size; in trench	35 m			

3.5 Example specification section

This is intended to be read in conjunction with the example drawing at 3.3 and the example quantities at 3.4.

As part of the CPI initiative the National Building Specification will be re-published in 1988 to comply with CAWS and this Project Specification Code. The selected example section has been based on a draft for the forthcoming new edition of NBS (kindly provided by NBS Ltd).

The proprietary names included in the example are fictitious.

R12   DRAINAGE BELOW GROUND   R12

To be read in conjunction with Preliminaries/General conditions.

INTRODUCTORY INFORMATION

010   DRAWINGS: The general scope and nature of the work is
       shown on the following drawings:
       - L(52)01 Drainage layout
       - L(52)02 Manhole schedule

020   EXISTING DRAINS:
       - Before starting work check invert levels and positions
         of existing drains, sewers, inspection chambers and
         manholes against information shown on drawings and
         report any discrepancies to CA.
       - Adequately protect existing live drains and maintain
         normal flows during construction.

TYPE(S) OF PIPELINE

101   PIPELINES FOR GENERAL USE:
       - Pipes, bends and junctions:
         Vitrified clay to BS 65, with flexible joints and
         Kitemark certified.
         Type: Normal
         Strength class: Super
         Sizes: 100 mm and 150 mm diameter
       - Assumed type of subsoil: Stiff to firm clay and sandy
         clay.
       - Bedding: Class D natural bedding, clause 340.

102   PIPELINES UNDER GROUND SLABS::
       - Pipes, bends and junctions:
         Vitrified clay as above.
         Size: 100 mm diameter.
       - Assumed type of subsoil: Compacted granular fill.
       - Bedding: Class X concrete surround, clause 460.

103   PIPELINES NEAR TO FOUNDATIONS:
       - Pipes, bends and junctions:
         Vitrified clay as above.
         Size: 100 mm diameter.
       - Assumed type of subsoil: Stiff to firm clay and sandy
         clay.
       - Bedding: Class X concrete surround, clauses 470 and
         480.

EXCAVATING/BACKFILLING

210   TRENCH WIDTH GENERALLY to be as small as practicable, but not less than external diameter of pipe plus 300 mm or larger dimension if specified. Trench sides must be vertical from bottom up to 300 mm above crown of pipe.

240   FORMATION FOR BEDS GENERALLY:
- Excavate immediately before laying beds or pipes.
- Remove mud, rock projections, boulders and hard spots and replace with approved filling material, well consolidated.
- Harden local soft spots by tamping in bedding material.
- Inform CA in advance to give him reasonable opportunity to inspect excavated formation for each section of the work.

260   TRENCH SUPPORTS: Remove trench supports and other obstacles sufficiently to permit compacted filling of all spaces.

270   BACKFILLING GENERALLY: Unless specified otherwise, backfill from top of specified surround or protective cushion with material excavated from the trench, laid and well compacted in layers not exceeding 300 mm thick. Do not use heavy compactors before there is 600 mm of material over pipes.

290   TEMPORARY BRIDGES: provide temporary bridges over trenches as necessary to prevent construction traffic damaging pipes after backfilling.

BEDDING/JOINTING

310   QUALITY OF WORK:
- Obtain pipes and fittings for each pipeline from the same manufacturer unless otherwise specified. Joint differing pipes and fittings with adaptors recommended by pipe manufacturer.
- Transport, store, bed and joint pipes, fittings and components in accordance with manufacturer's recommendations.
- Inspect all pipes and fittings carefully before laying and reject any which are defective. In particular ensure that spigots, couplings and ring seals are not chipped, damaged or dirty.
- Lay pipes singly, straight to line and true to gradient on an even bed for the full length of the barrel with sockets (if any) facing up the gradient.
- Joint using recommended lubricants, leaving recommended gaps at ends of spigots to allow for movement.
- Adequately protect pipelines from damage and ingress of debris. Seal all exposed ends of pipelines during construction.
- Arrange the work so as to minimise time between laying and testing.
- Carefully backfill immediately after successful testing.

340   CLASS D NATURAL BED:
- Excavate trench slightly shallower than the final levels.
- Hand trim to accurate levels, levelling up any over-dig
  with thoroughly compacted spoil. Where hand trimming is
  impracticable obtain instructions before proceeding.
- Cut holes in trench bottom for sockets/couplings and lay
  pipes resting uniformly on their barrels, adjusting to
  exact line and level. Do not use hard packings under pipes.
- After testing, backfill with a protective cushion of
  selected fill, free from vegetable matter, rubbish and
  frozen soil and excluding lumps and stones retained on
  a 40 mm sieve. Lay and thoroughly compact by hand in
  layers not exceeding 150 mm, to a level not less than
  150 mm above crown of pipe.

350   CLASS X CONCRETE SURROUND:
- Concrete: Mix E10/104 (Grade C20).
- Form vertical construction joints in surround at face
  of pipe joints at intervals of not more than 5 m using
  18 mm thick compressible board precut to finished
  profile of concrete and pipe. Fill any gap between
  spigot and socket with resilient material to prevent
  entry of concrete.
- Lay and compact bed of concrete over full width of
  trench to a level which will just clear pipe sockets/
  couplings, and allow to set.
- Lay pipes on concrete bed on folding timber wedges or
  on strip of fresh concrete to a level not less than 100
  mm above excavated trench bottom.
- After testing, place and compact further concrete for
  full width of trench to encase pipe up to a level 150
  mm above crown or to other levels as specified or shown
  on drawings.

460   SHALLOW RIGID PIPES UNDER SLABS: Where pipes (other than
plastics pipes) occur under concrete slabs and crown of
pipe is less than 150 mm below underside of slab, use
Class X concrete surround as specified above up to slab
formation level.

470   TRENCHES LESS THAN 1 M FROM FOUNDATIONS: Where bottom of
trench is lower than bottom of foundation, Class X
concrete surround as specified above to be used, top of
concrete being not lower than bottom of foundation.

480   TRENCHES MORE THAN 1 M FROM FOUNDATIONS: For the purpose
of this clause:
- Critical level = Z mm lower than level of foundation
  bottom.
- Z mm = distance from near side of drainage trench to
  foundation, minus 150 mm.
Where bottom of drainage trench is below critical level,
Class X concrete surround as specified above to be used,
top of concrete being not lower than critical level.

510   CONNECTION TO SEWERS: Connect new pipework to existing
sewers to satisfaction of local authority.

TERMINAL/ACCESS FITTINGS

610   PLAIN GULLY:
        Superpipe Ltd., two-piece gully, Code 158B/SS
        + low-back trap, plain-ended, Code 148A/SS
        + 150 mm square grid, Code 1002 (alloy).

611   HORIZONTAL BACK INLET GULLY:
        Superpipe Ltd., two-piece gully with 100 mm horizontal
        back inlet, Code 154B/SS
        + low-back trap, plain-ended, Code 148A/SS
        + 150 mm square grid, Code 1002 (alloy).

612   VERTICAL BACK INLET GULLY:
        Superpipe Ltd., two-piece gully with integral back inlet,
        Code 216/SS
        + low-back trap, plain-ended, Code 148A/SS
        + 150 mm square grid, Code 1002 (alloy).

613   VERTICAL BACK INLET ACCESS GULLY:
        Superpipe Ltd., one-piece gully, Code 191A/SS
        + sealing plate and frame, Code 1006 (alloy).

650   RODDING POINT:
        Superpipe Ltd., Code 262/SS with oval aluminium sealing
        plate and safety valve.

680   MANUFACTURE: Obtain each complete assembly of fittings,
        traps, etc., including appropriate couplings, from the
        same manufacturer, and check compatibility.

690   INSTALLATION:
        - Install fittings in accordance with manufacturers'
          recommendations.
        - Permissible deviation in level of gully gratings to be
          +0 -10 mm.
        - Set fittings square with and tightly jointed to
          adjacent construction as appropriate. If open to doubt
          obtain instructions.
        - Bed and surround fittings, traps, etc. in dry mix 1:3:6
          concrete, 150 mm thick.

MANHOLES/CHAMBERS/TANKS

710   BRICK MANHOLES/INSPECTION CHAMBERS:
        - Drawing reference(s): A(52)12-15.
        - Concrete base: Plain concrete, mix E10/104 (Grade C20).
        - Brickwork: Engineering, Type F10/106.
        - Step irons:
          Galvanized malleable cast iron to BS 1247.
          Bed in joints to all chambers over 900 mm deep at 300
          mm vertical centres staggered 300 mm horizontally, with
          the lowest step iron 300 mm above the benching and the
          top step iron 450 mm below the top of the cover.
        - Concrete slab:
          Precast or in situ at Contractor's discretion. If
          precast, bed solid in 1:3 mortar to brickwork.
          Concrete mix: E10/104.
          Reinforcement: Steel fabric to BS 4483, reference A142.
        - Access covers: Cast iron as clause 750.
        - Channels and benching: As clause 760.

740   PLASTICS INSPECTION CHAMBERS:
Manufacturer and reference:
Superpipe Ltd., Code PPIC with cast iron cover.
Bedding and surround: 100 mm granular material to BS 882.

750   CAST IRON MANHOLE COVERS AND FRAMES:
- To BS 497: Part 1 where applicable.
- Manufacturer: Torridon Iron Co. Ltd.
- Types:
  Roads and parking areas: Code 12 600 x 450 mm heavy
  duty covers, stainless steel locking bolts.
  Footpaths and paved areas: Code 130 600 x 450 mm medium
  duty covers, single seal filled with grease, stainless
  steel locking bolts, 1:1½:3 concrete filling, trowelled
  smooth.
- Bed frame solidly in 1:3 cement:sand mortar over its
  whole area, centrally over opening, level with
  surrounding finishes and square with joints in
  surrounding finishes or with the building.

760   CHANNELS, BRANCHES AND BENCHING:
- Bed channels and branches solid in 1:3 cement:sand
  mortar.
- Connect branches to main channel so that discharge
  flows smoothly in direction of main flow.
- Form benching in concrete to rise vertically from top
  of channels to a height not lower than soffit of outlet
  pipe, then slope upwards at 1 in 10 to walls. Within 3
  hours float with coat of 1:2 cement:sand mortar and
  finish smooth with steel trowel.

TESTING/COMPLETION

810   TESTING GENERALLY:
- Inform CA sufficiently in advance to give him a
  reasonable opportunity to attend all tests and
  inspections.
- Check that all sections of installation are free from
  obstruction and debris before testing.
- Provide clean water, assistance and apparatus for
  testing and inspection as required.
- Test all lengths of drain, manholes and inspection
  chambers under inspection of and to approval of local
  authority.
- Locate and remedy all defects without delay and retest
  as instructed.

840   AIR TESTING OF PIPELINES:
- Temporarily seal low ends of drains and connections.
- Connect glass 'U' tube water gauge to drain plug in
  length of drain under test.
- Pump air into test section until pressure equivalent to
  100 mm head of water is indicated, allowing time for
  air temperature to stabilise.
- Without further air being added, pressure must remain
  above equivalent of 75 mm head of water for not less
  than 5 minutes.

860   WATER TESTING OF MANHOLES/INSPECTION CHAMBERS: Test all
        brick manholes for watertightness not less than 4 weeks
        after backfilling and before practical completion as
        follows:
        - Temporarily seal all pipes entering chamber. To permit
          draining of test water, seal outlet pipe where it
          enters the next downstream chamber.
        - Fill chamber with clean water to a level 1.2 m above
          crown of outlet pipe or to top of chamber if less than
          1.2 m deep. Allow 2 to 4 hours for initial absorption
          and top up to test level before commencing test.
        - Water level must be maintained within 60 mm of original
          level for 30 minutes without adding further water.
        - If permitted loss is exceeded, re-test after a minimum
          period of two weeks. If permitted loss is exceeded at
          re-test, remedy defect before recommencing test
          sequence.

880   CLEANING: Flush out the whole installation and remove all
        silt and debris immediately before handing over.

3.6 Co-ordination on smaller projects

In general, smaller projects will require less information. The information will be provided by a smaller number of people so that problems of co-ordination between members of the design team will be minimised. The drawings may not need to be structured into different types and may be very few in number. There will probably be no bills of quantities. The specification will probably be significantly shorter than on large projects (see 5.5). It follows that co-ordination of project information on smaller projects is unlikely to be a severe problem. Nevertheless the technique of cross-referencing to the relevant sections and clauses of the specification will often be useful when annotating the drawings or writing the schedule of work.

The recommendation that all specification information be given in the project specification need not be taken too literally on smaller projects. Some kinds of work included in such projects may be of minor importance such that the writing of a specification section cannot be justified. Assuming that the specification for such items is brief, it can be given entirely on the drawings or schedule of work. The essential thing is to locate the whole specification for the type of work in one place in a form appropriate for both tendering and construction.

Again on smaller projects it may be found necessary (for economic reasons – see section 7.3) to use 'general' standard specifications, the variable specification information being given in the schedule of work and/or drawings. However many offices will find it desirable to prepare and present the specification and drawings for all jobs in the same way, including both with and without quantities contracts.

4 Specification techniques

4.1 Specification by performance or prescription

The specification process can be considered as two stages:

1. Ascertaining the performance required of the particular element, system, assembly, component or material.
2. Determining the products, materials and workmanship needed to meet the performance requirements, and stating any special conditions for carrying out the work.

The second of these stages is traditional *prescriptive specification*. If the project specification identifies only the performance requirements, leaving the manufacturer or contractor to determine the form and dimensions of the construction and/or the products, materials and workmanship, then this is known as *performance specification*. Specification by performance thus requires the manufacturer or contractor to complete the design process.

Performance specification for the building fabric

The concept of performance specification was developed in relation to materials and components for 'component building', being focused on the performance of products and components rather than the finished work in place (F). Standard product specifications, both BSI and proprietary, are increasingly written in terms of performance, this being of considerable help to the specifier when choosing products for incorporation into the work.

However this emphasis on performance specification of standard products has little impact on the way in which the typical project specification is used. Products are specified to comply with a particular standard and are purchased as such, invariably off the shelf – whether this standard is in terms of performance or prescription makes little difference to the contractor.

The choice between performance and prescriptive specification is more significant in project specification in respect of purpose made components (e.g. purpose made joinery) and materials (e.g. in situ concrete). The choice between the two approaches is influenced by the state of industry knowledge about the particular type of work. For example the properties, materials and workmanship of brickwork are often better understood by designers than bricklayers, so that normally specification is by prescription. On the other hand the properties, materials and workmanship of GRP cladding are understood fully by reputable specialist manufacturers, but usually not by designers, it being sensible to specify largely in terms of performance.

Performance specification for engineering services

For many years it has been normal practice to define the required performance of a system, produce outline drawings and a comprehensive specification and then require the contractor to develop the detailed design, install and commission the project and demonstrate that it will achieve the performance standards specified. Within the framework of the system many items of plant and equipment are specified by performance leaving the final selection to the contractor. However materials of common application such as pipework, insulation, cables and wiring are often specified by prescription.

A frequently used alternative is for a system to be specified almost entirely in terms of performance, the contractor undertaking the whole of the design in addition to selecting equipment, installing, commissioning and demonstrating compliance with the specified performance standards. Developments have also taken place where the designer has undertaken the detailed design, reducing the design involvement of the contractor. In these circumstances many pieces of equipment are still specified by performance requirements.

Practical limitations

In most areas of project specification both performance and prescriptive specification have strict practical limitations, and the following questions should be considered:

Performance specification:

- Can the specified standards be achieved at an acceptable cost?
- Are any of the specified requirements likely to be in conflict with each other in practical terms?
- Are reliable, economic and practical methods of test available?
- How can subjective requirements such as appearance be defined?
- Is the contractor/sub-contractor/supplier able to respond fully – has he enough skill and experience?
- Can the contractor's/sub-contractor's/supplier's design responsibility be recognised in the contract conditions, is it practicable to obtain a design warranty from him and is he suitably insured against design liability?
- Can the cost of responding (especially if competitive bids are invited) and establishing compliance be justified when set against the scale of the work?
- In cases where selection from competitive tenders on a value for money basis rather than just on price is desirable, will it be practicable?

Prescriptive specification:

- Will what has been specified function properly?
- Is the design the most practical and economic solution to the problem?
- Can it be verified that what has been specified has been provided?

It is clear that there are a lot of problems for the specifier. Devising an approach which provides effective quality control yet avoids the worst of the problems can be difficult. In practice the best available means of controlling quality will often be a mixture of prescriptive and performance specification. Whilst the two are often regarded as alternatives, they can be combined successfully provided the specifier has sufficient knowledge and skill to avoid practical conflicts.

4.2   Specification of options and alternatives

Performance specification should give the contractor, sub-contractor or supplier scope to exercise his design, constructional and commercial skills in order to achieve a satisfactory result at an acceptable cost. However, it should be borne in mind that many contractors do not purport to be designers. Prescriptive specification is, by definition, more restrictive for the contractor; however alternative products, methods, manufacturers and sub-contractors usually can be permitted. If more than one source of supply is permitted the contractor may be able to buy materials at a lower price and with a greater certainty that delivery dates will be met. Similarly, if given the choice, the contractor will be able to choose his sub-contractors on the basis of cost, time and reliability.

It is therefore recommended that wherever design priorities permit, the specification should permit options and alternatives. There are several ways of doing this, including:

Specifying products to comply with an industry standard

In most cases specifying to a British Standard will ensure that alternative manufacturers or suppliers are available to the contractor. However some British Standard grades or types are available from only one manufacturer, some are available only to special order, and some are not obtainable.

Where the British Standard or other document does not cover certain aspects, or sets too low a standard, the project specification can lay down supplementary requirements.

Specifying two or more proprietary products as alternatives

This may be appropriate where there is no industry standard, or where the standard is considered to be too low, or where appearance is very important. Specification of alternative proprietary products can sometimes be done indirectly by, for example, requiring an Agrément certified product. Another approach is to specify one or more proprietary products, followed by the phrase 'or equivalent' but this should be used only when the specifier is genuinely prepared to consider alternatives put forward by the contractor. In many cases the specifier may wish to permit alternatives but reserve his position on certain aspects, e.g. 'or equivalent of approved appearance'.

Permitting alternative sub-contractors or manufacturers of purpose made components

This can be done by giving a list of acceptable firms, or by imposing no restriction on source of supply. Where the preparation of tenders for such work is likely to be expensive, it is essential that all of the firms on the list have similar capability and approach to quality. This is especially important where the specification does not state the required quality in definitive terms or otherwise leaves aspects of quality open. Where the specification calls for detailed design to be completed by the sub-contractor or manufacturer, the firms on the list should be selected for their integrity and competence in both design and quality of work.

4.3 Specification by reference or description

Specification by reference to a published document, e.g. a British Standard, is an obvious way of reducing the amount of direct description in project documents, and therefore their bulk. It is relevant both to performance specification (e.g. testing in accordance with a certain BS) and prescriptive specification (e.g. natural slates to BS 680: Part 2).

Specification practice depends on frequent reference to industry documents, for otherwise project documents would be impossibly large and time consuming. Reference to well known standard documents can result in considerable saving of time particularly if there are no departures from the standard. Any such departures should be specifically (and prominently) described.

Despite the inherent advantages, specification by reference is characteristic of much bad practice, notably the use of blanket references to Codes of Practice which the specifier has not read, which the contractor will not have on site, and which in any case contain a variety of recommendations and options which ought to be decided on by the designer. Before deciding whether to specify by reference or description, the pros and cons should be considered:

- What is the status of the reference document? Is it authoritative? (in the sense of being technically sound rather than just having an official endorsement). Is it current? (in the sense of reflecting the best up to date practice rather than still being available).
- How readily available is the document? What does it cost? Does the contractor have to obtain the full document or can he safely rely on a summary such as BS Handbook No. 3? Alternatively can the contractor reasonably rely on his materials supplier or sub-contractor to have a copy of the document?
- How suitable is the document for use by the contractor and others? Is it couched in clear instructional terms? How much text is involved and is it easily identifiable in the document? If not, re-stating the relevant parts of the information in the project documents may be more convenient and effective.

- How much of the document does the specifier wish to invoke? It is undesirable to invoke a document then make specific exclusion of major parts. In principle it is better to refer specifically to the parts which apply or, in very complex cases, re-state the information in the project documents.

The circumstances in which the reference document will be used should also be borne in mind. For example clauses specifying the quality of products and materials are used mainly for estimating and ordering. These are mostly office activities, where reference documents should be available. Suppliers should have easy access to and a good working knowledge of the reference documents governing the products in which they trade. Site operatives do not need detailed specification of products, just a simple identification to make sure they fix the various products in their correct locations. It is therefore normal for clauses specifying products to refer extensively to British Standards and other documents.

The specification of workmanship is often less straightforward. Many of the available reference documents, e.g. Codes of Practice, are concerned with design guidance as well as workmanship, are often not sufficiently definitive for contractual purposes and are rarely available on building sites. Further, site personnel should not be left to resolve the alternatives, options and doubts which can be left open by such documents, it being preferable to spell out requirements in full. To be suitable for reference on site, documents need to be uncomplicated, definitive and readily available. Specification of workmanship by reference is discussed in greater detail in Section 5.4.

4.4 How to specify by reference

The main principles to follow are:

- Refer to a document substantially or not at all. Remember that acquisition of documents can be costly and time consuming for the contractor, so do not invoke just a small part of a substantial document.
- Identify the document precisely, giving title, publisher, date, reference number as appropriate. Ensure that the date of the current edition is not open to doubt.
- Be familiar with the contents of the document – otherwise the references are likely to be over-generalised, inappropriate or contradictory.
- Be helpfully precise, stating the part, chapter, type, grade, class, group, quality, section, table, column, material, finish, clause, appendix, code, weight, size, number or other designation(s) which apply.
- Do not specify by reference to two documents which have a confused or contradictory relationship.
- Ensure that supplementary specification does not duplicate or contradict the reference document, e.g. specifying a minimum cement content for a BS 5328 ordinary prescribed concrete mix.

British Standards

It has been customary to generalise certain aspects of specification by reference, for example the dates and revisions of British Standards are frequently required to be those current at (say) the date of invitation of tenders. This avoids the considerable chore of updating references to British Standards and their amendments, and permits considerable simplification of the text – compare the following alternatives:

- 'UPVC pipes, bends and junctions: to BS 4660: 1973 + Amendments AMD 2514, AMD 3708, AMD 4006, AMD 4081, AMD 4441 or BS 5481: 1977 + Amendments AMD 3631, AMD 4435.'
- 'UPVC pipes, bends and junctions: to BS 4660 or BS 5481'.

However the practice encourages specifiers not to check on the latest revisions and amendments and fails to recognise the difficulty of establishing the exact dates of publication. As a balanced compromise, a preliminaries clause on the following lines is suggested:

'REFERENCES TO BSI DOCUMENTS are to the versions and amendments listed in the BSI Catalogue 19   and any subsequent versions and amendments specifically referred to in the project specification.'

Manufacturer's recommendations

It has also been customary to generalise references to manufacturer's recommendations for storage, handling, fixing, etc. Difficulties can arise if the manufacturer's recommendations are inadequate, or out of date, or not readily available, or if the contractor and designer are working to different reference documents. Therefore wherever practicable specific reference should be made to particular items of literature produced by product manufacturers. (Manufacturer's Sitework Instructions and other documents should have clear titles, unique references and dates of publication as recommended in BS 4940: 1973, 4.5 et seq.)(G).

(F) 'Performance Specification Writing for Building Components' MOPBW, D.C.9, 1969.

(G) BS 4940 Recommendations for the presentation of technical information about products and services in the construction industry'.

5 What should be specified?

5.1 General

Specification information should be given for each type of work using the checklists given in Part B so far as they are applicable to the particular project. Alternatively a suitable library of specification clauses may be used (see 7.3). The nature of the specification information to be given will vary, it being possible to identify the following types:

- Standard products and materials
- Purpose made components and assemblies
- Workmanship.

In writing the project specification, the guidance on specification techniques set out in section 4 should be followed.

5.2 Standard products and materials

The terms 'standard' and 'purpose made' need to be defined. Taken literally, 'standard' means to be uniform, following a set pattern. 'Purpose made' means made to order purposely for a specific project or application. The two terms overlap in that:

- there is a wide range of products which are not designed specially for the project, being 'standard' in the sense of complying with an industry, trade or proprietary specification, but which are made to order rather than supplied ex stock;
- many components complying with a standard specification can in practice be made by a competent joiner, metalworker or concretor, as if they were 'purpose made';
- many published standards relate only to standard of construction, others only to some aspects of performance, others only to dimensions – in other respects the products may be purpose designed;
- many manufacturers can be persuaded to alter their proprietary standards if the order is large enough.

For the purposes of this document standard products are taken to mean those which might be expected to be available ex stock, being specified mainly by reference to an industry specification, or by proprietary designation as set out in manufacturer's literature. It is vital for the designer to identify the specification variants which are on offer and to state his choice (e.g. size, colour, rating, strength) using the designations and terms used in the BS or by the manufacturer. The information should be sufficiently definitive to permit ordering of the materials. Where a proprietary product which is not generally known in the industry is specified, it is helpful to give the manufacturer's full name, address and telephone number.

5.3 Purpose made components and assemblies

Manufacturers of purpose made components usually know far more than the designer about the detailed methods of fabrication and often have their own preferred ways of doing things. It is thus likely to be advantageous if the specification is concerned with the quality of the end product rather than the means of achieving it.

Variability of industry Standards

The project specification for such work will vary according to the degree to which industry Standards have been developed. Some very different examples can be observed:

- Ready mixed concrete is governed by BS 5328 and the Quality Scheme for Ready Mixed Concrete (QSRMC). The product can therefore be specified concisely and with confidence, normally by performance.
- Purpose made joinery is governed by BS 1186: Parts 1 and 2 supplemented by the standards for adhesives (BS 1204) and preservative treatment (BS 5589). All of these documents have a bias towards performance, but some aspects of high quality work are not covered. Specification of high quality purpose made joinery is therefore relatively complex, involving reference to several documents and introduction of additional workmanship information. There are no industry quality assurance schemes, so specification involves a degree of risk.
- Non-loadbearing precast concrete cladding is covered by CP 297: 1972, which gives guidance in rather general terms. The PSA Method of Building Guide MOB 01.704 1978 gives specific and relevant design guidance. Many of the BSI and Cement and Concrete Association publications dealing with concrete and reinforcement are relevant. Panel joints and fixings are covered by several BRE Digests and BSs. There is thus a large amount of official published information; the problem is discriminating between the good and the not so good, and attempting to co-relate and select from the recommendations of many documents written at different times, often from different points of view.
- Glass reinforced plastics cladding is not covered by a British Standard or Code of Practice and trade documents are fragmentary and of poor standard. Substantial project specification is therefore necessary, relying on standards adapted from textiles, precast concrete, painting, etc., with much special text. In the absence of quality control schemes, selection of reputable manufacturers is vital.

Typical specification content

Detailed design of purpose-made components is often left to specialist manufacturers or sub-contractors. It is likely that the work will be contracted on a design and manufacture basis with some kind of warranty agreement between the sub-contractor and building owner. The specification and drawings on which tenders are invited are likely to be relatively 'open' with a bias towards performance. The specification is likely to cover the following:

- Definition of the scope of work, including design, manufacture, fixing, finishing, accessories, etc. It is usual to require 'completion' of the design from the drawings and specification provided.
- Definition of the procedures, submissions and approvals which are required, e.g. information to be submitted with tender, shop drawings, mock-ups and small samples, production control units, inspection before final fixing.
- Required compliance with appropriate Codes of Practice, and requirements for selected properties, e.g. fire test rating, U value, load bearing capacity, permissible deflection.
- Evidence required to demonstrate compliance, e.g. calculations, reference to previously constructed buildings, submission of samples, records of previous destructive tests, tests required for this project.
- Basic materials and workmanship specification to cover aspects of quality which are not adequately controlled by other means.

5.4 Workmanship

The main problem with specification of workmanship is to know how much detail to give. This is particularly so with the traditional trades where designers often have a considerable practical knowledge. A paradoxical situation exists in that:

- Large jobs involve a lot of money, so there is an incentive to produce thorough, detailed information. Designers on large jobs usually have more time to be thorough, and contractors have more time to assimilate the information. But larger contractors should have more knowledge and better systems of quality control and supervision, and therefore have less need of detailed workmanship specification.
- Small jobs involve less risk, there is less time available, but perhaps the need for detailed workmanship clauses is greater.

Specification of workmanship by reference

British Standard 8000 'Workmanship on building sites' (WOBS) is in course of preparation. It is expected that it will give recommendations for basic workmanship for the more common types of building work, but it will not cover more specialised types of work and engineering services. If the Standard comes to be generally available on building sites (i.e. unlike most Codes of Practice), it should be practicable to exclude a great deal of standard workmanship text from project specifications, which could then concentrate on 'special' workmanship items. Variations in amount of workmanship specification for the work sections included in WOBS would thus be related to the complexity and special quality requirements rather than (as previously) the scale of the work.

A similar development, of particular value in areas not covered by WOBS, is the progressive improvement in manufacturers' published sitework instructions. Where these exist and are of good quality, they can be invoked by reference, thus reducing the need for detailed workmanship clauses in the project specification. Manufacturers' sitework instructions should comply with BS 4940.(H)

Specification of workmanship by description

For those sections of the project specification not covered by WOBS or good quality manufacturers' information, it will normally be appropriate to provide a relatively full specification of workmanship requirements. Published libraries of specification clauses complying with this Code can be used to ensure:

- a degree of industry standardisation in how far to take the workmanship descriptions;
- economy of language so that the workmanship specification is not excessively bulky.

There are considerable difficulties in specifying the appearance of many kinds of finished work, e.g. brickwork, concrete finishes, rendering. The materials to be used, joint profiles, depth of exposure of aggregates, etc. can be specified with precision, but the finer qualities of colour, texture, consistency, etc. usually defy meaningful description. Use of photographs and reference to existing samples and buildings is recommended, provided these are clear and accessible. It is good practice to specify the construction of samples on site for approval of appearance before the remainder of the work is put in hand. Such samples, which may be special mock-ups or part of the finished work, should be of adequate size and incorporate important features so that they are meaningful and helpful in establishing acceptable standards of appearance.

5.5 When the specification needs to be brief

It must be recognised that many small builders and sub-contractors are working directors operating without separate estimating and management staff, often coping with the paperwork in their spare time. Brevity is thus desirable in specifications for smaller jobs.

However to think in terms of 'large jobs' and 'small jobs' can be misleading. Many small jobs include one or two types of work with a disproportionately high value. Equally, most large jobs include some types of work of quite low value and importance. It therefore makes sense to vary the size of the specification on a section by section basis, as well as project to project.

In considering specifications for small scale work, there are some strange paradoxes:

- As described in Part 5.4, there is perhaps a greater need for detailed specification of workmanship.
- It cannot be assumed that the required quality is lower – often the reverse is true.
- Nor can it be assumed that the work is less complex, and it is complexity rather than scale of the work which affects the size of a specification.
- Specification by reference to other documents can reduce the size of a specification enormously, but small contractors are less likely to have the documents.
- Small specifications do not necessarily take less time to prepare, indeed when using a comprehensive library of clauses (see 7.3) the time taken tends to be related to the proportion of clauses deleted rather than those included.

Whilst there can be little doubt that specifications for such work need to be relatively brief, they have probably been excessively so in traditional practice. As with specifications generally, there is a strong case for increasing their technical content as compared with traditional practice.

Specifications for smaller projects can be kept reasonably brief by:

- Concentrating on the more important types of work included in the project. Minor items of work may be excluded from the specification, being covered by brief notes on the drawings or description in the schedule of work (if any).
- Specifying standard rather than purpose-made products and assemblies – the latter involve much more substantial specification, and in any case are often difficult to justify for small works.
- Specifying in a more general, less specifically detailed way, and leaving out clauses which have marginal relevance.

Such specifications will define the required quality of work in a less precise and comprehensive way. Other aspects of quality control should therefore be considered carefully, including the quality of the drawings and/or schedule of works and selection of reliable contractors.

(H) BS 4940 'Recommendations for the presentation of technical information about products and services in the construction industry'.

6 Arrangement and presentation of the specification

6.1 Arrangement of the specification into work sections

In common with the quantities, the specification is used by a wide variety of people and organisations. The main contractor and clerk of works will need to have easy reference to the complete specification, but most of the people involved will be sub-contractors and suppliers who are concerned only with parts of the specification. It is vital that the specification is arranged into sections which reflect these sub-contract groupings. This will make it easier for the main contractor to divide up the documents for distribution to sub-contractors and suppliers in order to obtain estimates and arrange for the construction of the various types of work.

The Common arrangement of work sections (CAWS) has been devised with this in mind and is recommended for use in the UK on all types of project in preference to any other method of arrangement. Its use will give good co-ordination with quantities prepared in accordance with SMM7 and following the SMM7 recommendations on arrangement. CAWS includes detailed definitions of the contents of the work sections in order to give greater predictability as to the location of sundry items. Each work section should be as self-contained as practicable. The alpha/numeric sequence of CAWS should facilitate looking up of specification cross-references given on the drawings and other documents.

6.2 Arrangement within the work sections

An example project specification section for below ground drainage is given at 3.5. It illustrates the principles of cross-referencing and arrangement of information within work sections described in this section.

The internal arrangement of the specification work sections should be designed to give easy access to and assimilation of the information. When reading a work section, the information should appear to be orderly and coherent, with helpful headings which accurately reflect their contained text. For much of the time specifications are used like an encyclopedia, to check on particular materials or other requirements; good headings and keywords are essential if such isolated pieces of information are to be found easily.

Section 3.2 of this Code recommends that the amount of specification information given on drawings and schedules and in bills of quantities should be limited, cross-reference being made to the appropriate part of the specification. It follows that an overriding consideration in the arrangement of specifications is the need for them to be referred to easily, and for the contents to be co-related speedily and certainly with the drawings, quantities and schedules.

In this respect the traditional arrangement of specification clauses under main headings for 'Materials' and 'Workmanship' is unlikely to work well. This is because drawings and bills of quantities show and measure things in terms of finished work in place, involving separate specification clause references for the principle materials, secondary materials and different aspects of workmanship. Referencing is likely to be made much simpler if these specification statements are brought together in composite or 'two part' descriptions. However in some cases this ideal cannot be achieved without repetition, and a reasonable balance has to be struck between convenience in use and bulk of text.

In services installations the amount of repetition from one 'system' to another will often be so great as to necessitate heavy reliance on reference to separate 'reference specification' sections (CAWS Group Y). Further, the possible combinations of materials and workmanship requirements for services are so numerous that merging the two together is usually impractical.

The optimum arrangement within building fabric work sections will vary depending on the subject matter, for example:

- Where the work section contains two or more separate kinds of work, these may be dealt with in different sub-sections (e.g. P10 Sundry insulation/proofing work/fire stops).
- Where the work section contains both performance and prescription specification, the two may be separated into different sub-sections (e.g. H41 GRP cladding/features).
- Where the work section contains important items which are measured differently, these may be arranged in different sub-sections (e.g. general areas (m^2) and edge details (linear) for H62 Natural slating).
- Clauses may be divided into sub-sections for materials and workmanship where this is not, in practice, a significant obstacle to easy cross-referencing (e.g. E30 Reinforcement for in situ concrete, in which the only significant specification variant for purposes of cross-referencing is the type of reinforcement.)
- Sub-section headings may reflect a series of operations (e.g. M10 Sand cement/Concrete/Granolithic screeds/flooring, with headings for Preparation – Laying – Finishing).

These basic variations often occur in combination, so that virtually every section will be arranged in a unique way. Despite this variability of sub-section headings certain basic types of specification clauses or items can be identified as follows:

Introductory information

These are clauses which relate to the section as a whole, being of a procedural, contractual and administrative nature. Work sections which are normally the subject of specialist sub-contracting will tend to have several such clauses, e.g:

- General description and scope of work.
- List of relevant drawings.
- Information to be submitted with tenders.
- Requirements for submission of shop drawings and other information.
- Advance checking, inspecting or surveying of existing work.

Work type clauses

These are clauses which serve to define the main types of work included in the section, for example:

E10 In situ concrete – types of mix
F10 Brick/block walling – types of walling
R12 Drainage below ground – types of pipeline (see section 3.5).

The work type clauses show the way in which the main specification variants are combined. For example in the case of drainage pipelines, the main variants are likely to be as follows:

- Pipes: vitrified clay, concrete, cast iron or plastics, each with a range of quality options and sizes.
- Ground conditions: these may vary from one part of the site to another or at different depths. Variations may affect ease of excavation, the need for

earthwork support and the type of bedding for the pipes.

- Bedding: a wide range of standard beddings can be used depending on type and size of pipe, type of subsoil, load on ground surface, depth and width of trench.

The whole point of these work type clauses is to define the way in which such variants are combined, in order to assist rapid assimilation. Where the specification variants involve significant amounts of repetitive text, this can be included elsewhere in the specification and a cross-reference given.

Aspects of the work types which are not specification variants can be excluded from the type items and covered by standard general clauses elsewhere in the specification. For example excavation and backfilling of drainage trenches can usually be covered in this way.

Clauses to support the work type clauses

As described above these may be either:

- specific 'variant' clauses which are relatively long, e.g. a particular type of bedding for a drainage pipeline. There is considerable advantage if such clauses are self-contained so that they can be invoked in the work type clauses by a single cross-reference, or
- general clauses dealing with matters which are not normally 'variants' e.g., in the case of drainage, excavation and backfilling, testing and inspection.

Examples of such clauses are included in the sample project specification at 3.5.

Accessories and equipment

These, by their very nature, tend to be clauses which are not closely linked to other parts of the specification. Examples would be drainage gullies, manholes, inspection chambers. Here again there is advantage in making these clauses as self contained as possible so that they can be invoked by single specific cross-references from drawings and bills of quantities, e.g. 'Horizontal back inlet gully, R12/611' (see section 3.5).

6.3 Language of specifications

Specifications usually are substantial documents which can take a long time to read and use. There is a wide-spread desire to keep them as brief as possible. Brevity can be achieved by using an economical style, judicious use of specification by reference, and saying only that which needs to be said, for example:

- Do not repeat things covered in the contract.
- Do not repeat information already specified by reference to another document.
- Do not anticipate remote contingencies by lengthy provisions.
- Use generic description in preference to exhaustive examples.
- Avoid special emphasis as it rarely helps and can imply that other things are not important.
- Leave out needless 'justificatory' explanation; however where the objective of an instruction may not be clear to the contractor, it may be helpful to state it.

It is important to think in terms of time rather than quantity of paper – the former is expensive, the latter relatively cheap. Put another way, the clarity and ease of use of a document is more important than its length although that also is important.

Clarity and simplicity of style can save time for both specifier (when editing a basic text) and contractor. The main principles are as follows:

LENGTH OF CLAUSES: Strike a balance between too short (staccatto) and too long (rambling). Two to six lines is about right, but can be longer if the clause is sub-itemised.

SUB-ITEMISATION can be used to:
- break up a long clause, making it easier to read;
- set out a series of attributes or properties;
- describe a series of sub-operations;
- set out a range of options or alternatives.

KEYWORDS: Each clause should have one or more words in upper case at the beginning, chosen to reflect the subject of the clause in order to assist scanning of pages to find relevant clauses.

PRODUCTS CLAUSE KEYWORDS will usually be the generic name of the material or product.

WORKMANSHIP CLAUSE KEYWORDS will usually be nouns, e.g. the material being fixed, the feature of the work being constructed, the name of the operation. Usually it is unhelpful to choose a verb as the keyword, e.g. 'FIX stair nosings with . . . .'

COVERAGE OF CLAUSES: Each clause should be about a specific topic so that it lends itself to clear and helpful keywording.

SEQUENCE OF CLAUSES: Clauses should be in a clear, rational sequence in context with the headings. This should show through in the keywording.

TWO PART CLAUSE CONSTRUCTION: First state the subject of the clause, followed by a colon, followed by the qualitative statement about that subject. Thus in products clauses the colon will have the meaning 'shall be'.

TERSENESS: Write directly and briefly, giving necessary information and no more.

'THE CONTRACTOR SHALL' and similar phrases are not necessary.

TERMINOLOGY: Where appropriate use terms defined in BS 6100 'Glossary of building and civil engineering terms'.

DEFINED TERMS (e.g. 'Architect', 'approval', 'or equivalent approved') should be used consistently throughout.

QUALITY OF WRITING: Simple, clear and elegant language is difficult to achieve. Use of well written, carefully considered standard clauses can offer significant advantages over writing from scratch.

7 Producing the specification

7.1 Who should prepare the specification?

The designer is responsible for the preparation of the specification. On many smaller projects there may be only one professional adviser, usually an architect or building surveyor. On most larger projects there will be a number of design disciplines – architect, structural engineer, services engineer, landscape architect, etc. Each designer should prepare the specification for the types of work for which he has responsibility. Some topics may have divided responsibility and need to be tackled jointly, e.g. load-bearing facing brickwork.

Within the architect's and engineer's offices it is important that the various sections of the specification are written by the most appropriate people. The project architect or project engineer or a suitably qualified assistant under his close control and who is fully conversant with the project should normally undertake the task. However, other people within the office may have special knowledge of certain kinds of work and can give useful advice and/or check the relevant sections of the draft specification.

An alternative approach is for the specification to be prepared by a specification writer within the design office. Such a person may be expected to have considerable expertise and should help to give consistency to the office's specification practice. However with this approach careful checking is particularly important to ensure that the specification reflects the needs of the job and is consistent with the information shown on the drawings.

Design teams often draw a sharp distinction between projects to be tendered on a 'with quantities' basis and those which are to be without quantities. However it is important to recognise that the position of the designer does not differ between the with and without quantities situations. In both, he is concerned to produce graphic and descriptive instructions to be followed by the contractor during construction. The use of a bill of quantities to obtain tenders and as a basis for the financial management of the project should have little effect on the form, content and authorship of the drawings and specification.

The architect, structural engineer, services engineer, quantity surveyor and other specialists may contribute to the preparation of the complete specification. It is therefore important that the design team leader should co-ordinate the whole process, including:

- deciding who is to do what, and when;
- monitoring progress and ensuring that target dates are met;
- ensuring that technical and editorial checking of drafts is carried out;
- ensuring that the whole document is consistent with the design aims and the drawings, and is appropriate to the nature of the project.

7.2 The need for knowledge and information

The specification for a building project of average size and average complexity contains a large amount of information. References to British Standards and proprietary products will invoke a much larger volume of printed material. There is perhaps as much material again which is not invoked by the specification but which is available as useful and relevant advice to the specifier. This mass of published information is changing constantly, on average at about 20% per annum.

The sheer volume of this information is such that the individual designer cannot assimilate it all. Corporate action by the design office is necessary, by:

- encouraging individuals within the office to develop special expertise on certain topics – in this way a team of designers can cover a wide range of technical subjects and give detailed advice to each other on the specifications for their respective current projects;
- operating an efficient technical library, with adequate updating – the library will be far more effective if it is selective, including only high quality information relating to tried and tested products and processes;
- maintaining a suitable up to date library of specification clauses and guidance notes.

7.3 Libraries of clauses

Researching and writing clear, succinct specification clauses from scratch is a very time consuming process. It is necessary for economic reasons to re-use sound specification clauses on many projects. Given that such clauses are the best which can be devised, there are obvious technical advantages in using them repeatedly, adapting them only where special circumstances apply.

If such clauses are well researched and specifically written for convenience in editing, the task of producing high quality project specifications can be made much easier. Such text is usually described as a 'library of specification clauses' and to be fully effective needs to have the following features:

- It should follow the principles set out in this Code.
- The clauses should present the designer with a clearly sequenced set of options and alternatives which relate well to the design choices which are available. The designer can thus prepare the bulk of his project specification by selecting appropriate clauses. Variable information can be dealt with by leaving gaps at appropriate places in the standard clauses for the designer to insert appropriate details.
- The clauses should be written in a disciplined way so that each one is about a particular aspect or feature of the work. They will thus normally be smaller and more numerous than traditional clauses, and will lend themselves to clear titling or 'keywording' as recommended at 6.3.
- Both clauses and guidance notes should be thoroughly researched and well written so that the library of clauses is straightforward to use and the designer rarely feels the need to alter the standard wording.
- The technical coverage should include all commonly occurring types of work. Only rarely, if ever, should the designer find it necessary to write a section of his specification from scratch because it is not included in the library of clauses.
- Clauses for smaller, simpler jobs should be included, in order to facilitate production of relatively brief specifications. Ideally, these clauses should be available as a separate version of the library of clauses.
- The clauses should be arranged by CAWS, observing the detailed section definitions. Within the work sections the clauses should be arranged in accordance with the principles described in 6.2
- Both clauses and guidance notes should be updated regularly, drawing the designer's attention to changes in key technical documents.
- The clauses should be suitable for use with computers and word processors, and should be available on disk.

The preparation and maintenance of such a library of clauses requires a formidable amount of effort, and only the largest design offices will be able to contemplate doing it for themselves. For most offices it will be necessary to consider subscribing to a commercially available library of clauses, which complies with the criteria listed above. This will have the advantage of reducing needless variation between the project specifications produced by different design offices.

However, design offices do not have to accept and use commercially available libraries of clauses without modification. It is possible for the office to edit the basic text into an 'office' library of clauses in order to:

- make it more directly related to the technical preferences of the office, by adding special clauses and deleting others;
- reduce the time taken in preparing project specifications, by reducing the number of options and alternatives and the amount of information to be inserted – the reduction in time taken may be necessary to meet tight pre-contract programmes, or to reduce costs in the designer's office;
- apply greater control to the technical output of the office, for example by standardising the choice of proprietary products wherever possible.

Modifying the basic library in this way can involve a lot of work, not least in coping with updating. It can also involve compromises in the quality of finished project specifications, but equally may give improvements. Before embarking on such a policy offices should establish beyond reasonable doubt that the benefits will clearly outweigh the difficulties.

The alternative is to use the commercially available library of clauses without modification. An increasingly adopted variant on this is to create supplementary guidance notes – this approach avoids the difficulties of modifying the whole library, yet enables the office to influence the way it is used. The supplementary notes can cover virtually anything, e.g. preferred proprietary products, products and practices to be avoided, additional advice on use of clauses, suggested text for supplementary clauses.

The use of an appropriate library of specification clauses is recommended. Section 7.4 describes a model procedure for preparing a project specification and assumes the use of such a library.

7.4 A model procedure

Specifying is an integral part of the design process and can be carried out most easily and effectively concurrently with preparation of the drawings. Decisions on specification start to be made early – the client's brief often contains specific instructions and preferences, and other firm decisions are prompted by the obtaining of statutory approvals for the project. The majority of firm decisions on materials and workmanship should be taken before completion of detailed design. The specification should be completed before inviting tenders.

At the beginning of the detailed design stage a clear plan for the production of the project specification should be made. A list of the specification sections should be prepared and, assuming that a library of clauses is to be used, an up to date expendable copy of those sections should be obtained. Any special sections not covered by the library of clauses should be identified and thought given as to how they are to be tackled. Responsibility for writing each section should be decided, paying particular attention to those sections which will involve joint responsibility (see 7.1).

The procedure for each section of the specification will be basically the same. The library of clauses and accompanying guidance notes should be read. If the designer is not thoroughly familiar with the Codes of Practice and other relevant reference documents, he should obtain them and read the relevant parts (see 7.2). This part of the procedure can be time consuming and will usually vary widely from section to section. The newly acquired knowledge may prompt revision of certain design assumptions and may affect the drawings as well as the specification. Before becoming deeply involved in the detail of the specification, the choice of materials and methods of construction should be reviewed in the context of user requirements and budget.

All specification decisions should be systematically recorded at the time they are made. This can be done by marking up an expendable copy of the library by clauses, building up the project specification clause by clause.

As the clauses are marked up the accompanying guidance notes should be checked and relevant British Standards and manufacturers' literature consulted. Clauses for 'work types' and accessories (see section 6.2) will need to be decided on at a fairly early stage in order that cross-references to the specification can be put on the drawings.

In marking up the library of clauses one should be both decisive and clear. The purpose of writing a specification is to give useful information, and there is little point in producing a specification which fails to do this. Compare the following clauses:

420   PRESERVATIVE TREATMENT FOR <u>TRUSSES AND PURLINS</u>:
       Preservative: <u>Protim 80</u>
       Application: <u>Medium hazard specification of Protim Ltd.</u>

420   PRESERVATIVE TREATMENT FOR <u>TIMBER</u> _ _ _ _ _ _ _ _ _:
       Preservative: <u>to approval</u>
       Application: <u>pressure</u>

The marking up of the library of clauses may be carried out intermittently over several days or even weeks. At the end of the process it is important to check through to ensure that the specification has been completed. This will be facilitated if the method of marking up distinguishes clearly between:

- Clauses which have been deleted
- Clauses which have been included
- Clauses about which no decision has been taken

An example of such a method is illustrated below.

---

(203) SUITABILITY OF BASE: before starting work ensure roof is to correct falls and all preliminary work, including formation of grooves, provisions of battens and upstands and fixing of roof outlets to correct levels is complete. Base must be clean and dry. Sub-contractor must confirm to Main Contractor and SO his agreement that the base is suitable.

Clause included

207   EXISTING ASPHALT ROOFING:
       1. Before starting work agree with SO the extent and nature of repairs to be carried out.
       2. Remove _ _ _ _ _ _ _ _ _ _ _, dust, dirt and grease.
       3. Remove any moss and treat surfaces with fungicide.
       4. Carefully cut out asphalt around cracks and blisters back to a sound edge. Replace with roofing asphalt ensuring complete fusion with existing asphalt.
       5. Prime all surfaces to which insulation is to be bonded.

Decision not yet taken

~~211~~   KEYING TO SLOPING/VERTICAL CONCRETE (surfaces more than 10° from horizontal): Either:
       1. remove surface laitance by washing and brushing while still green, or
       2. remove all mould oil and apply keying primer or keying mix.

Clause deleted

Assuming that a printed copy of the library of clauses is being marked up by hand for subsequent typing or word processing, a good deal of clarity is needed in recording decisions. Writing should be clear. Printing in upper case letters (as if annotating a drawing) is unhelpful – remember that the specification will be typed in upper and lower case. Pay particular attention to technical terms and proprietary names and references – the typist may not be familiar with these.

On completion, each section of the specification should be reviewed in general terms – is it too thorough and onerous – or is it insufficiently detailed and exacting? Does it relate satisfactorily to other sections?

When bills of quantities are prepared, the programme for supply of information to the quantity surveyor should provide for both drawings and specification sections. Drawings of certain parts of the building will relate closely to certain specification sections and they should be brought to an appropriate state of completion at the same time. It is usually advantageous to supply the specification to the quantity surveyor in draft form, because he will be the first user of the specification, and is therefore likely to discover any errors, discrepancies or omissions. It is far better that he discovers and raises these with the designer before the specification is finalised.

7.5 Presentation of the specification

The arrangement and language of the specification will be largely predetermined if a library of specification clauses is used. However other aspects of presentation of the specification are more likely to be decided by the design team, e.g. typing, printing and binding; these are worth considering carefully for they can make or mar the end product.

A typical design office may produce hundreds or even thousands of pages of job specification in one year. It is therefore worth standardising practice on such things as margins, headings, continuation headings, indenting, spacing and page numbering, insisting on high visual standards.

Even when the specification is word processed, checking of the finished document is still necessary to ensure that the modifications to the basic text have been carried out correctly. Proof-reading is a tedious task, but also a difficult one – it should be carried out by someone who is known from experience to be good at it. There will be some advantage if the proof-reading is done by a member of the design team because he or she is likely to spot errors or discrepancies contained in the marked-up draft and reproduced in the finished document.

CAWS has been designed to help contractors divide up the contents of project documents for distribution to specialist sub-contractors. To facilitate this it is recommended that each specification work section starts on a new page; the alternative of running the sections on will usually give only a small reduction in the total number of pages.

Given that each section starts on a new page, each page in the specification will be devoted to only one section. This means that each page can be 'flagged' by typing the work section number in the top outside corner to help users find sections quickly.

A contents page or pages should be provided preferably with sections indexed to page numbers. Page numbers should preferably run consecutively throughout the document to facilitate checking that pages are not missing.

The total thickness of a document is often thought to be important. This can be minimised by typing onto A3 paper, then photo-reducing to A4. Printing on both sides of the paper will also reduce the apparent size but will make the specification more difficult to sub-divide for distribution to sub-contractors.

The specification will need to be read with the measured quantities or schedule of work. This will be facilitated if these different types of information are in separate volumes so that they can be opened side by side. Thumbing backwards and forwards within a single volume can be inconvenient.

It is important that the project specification is incorporated as a contract document. This will be automatic under some forms of contract, but in other cases it will be necessary to ensure that the project specification is titled and numbered as one of the contract bills of quantities, e.g. 'Bill number 2: Specification'. Alternatively it can be divided up as specification preambles to the various sections of measured work.

Specifications are relatively large documents, densely packed with information and, no matter how elegantly arranged and written, they can be rather heavy reading. Good presentation can make them much easier to use. Unfortunately presentation is often skimped with a view to saving money. It is worth bearing in mind that the cost of word processing and printing a typical project specification is likely to be only about one tenth of the cost of the professional time invested in writing it. Cheeseparing on presentation can all too easily become a false economy.

The first consideration is typing or word processing. Specification text lends itself to a high degree of standardisation and thus also to word processing. There are likely to be cost savings compared with conventional typing, particularly if the reduced cost of proof-reading is taken into account. The greatest benefit from word processing is likely to be a much greater freedom from typing errors, these being concentrated in those parts of the text not generated from the magnetic memory.

The choice of word processing hardware and software should be considered carefully. The visual quality of the type produced by the printer should be at least as good as that used in correspondence. Software features to be considered, include:

Essential Features
- Upper and lower case
- A4 page width and length
- Storage of text in separate jobs/records/files varying in size between 1 page and 30 pages
- Recall of individual pages
- Duplication from a master file
- Permanent set ups for page formats
- Automatic adjustment of line breaks consequent upon text changes
- Underscoring

Optional Features
- Recall of individual clauses
- 'Find' facility for characters, words and phrases
- Hyphenation prompting at line breaks
- Right hand justification
- Proportional spacing
- Emboldening of headings
- 'Stop' instruction to find variable text positions
- Format variation within text
- A3 page width and length
- Automatic page numbering
- Checking of spelling
- Automatic insertion of continuation headings, job numbers, etc.
- Highlighting of changes from the previous draft

Sufficient copies of the project specification should be printed for tender, contractual and record purposes, formal submissions, copies for the client, working copies for all consultants, the clerk of works and the contractor. It is all too easy to under-estimate the contractor's needs – remember that the specification will not be consulted if copies are not available at the appropriate times and places. In addition to bound reference copies, a number of loosely tagged copies will usually be useful to the contractor for splitting up and distributing to subcontractors.

Part B

Guidance on coverage

The following checklists give guidance on the content of project specifications* and preliminaries, set out in the Common arrangement of work sections (CAWS).

The checklists give the subject matter or headings for typical clauses but do not necessarily give sub-headings which might appear within clauses. For example in section F10 the item for bricks/blocks does not list properties which may be relevant, e.g. permeability, crushing strength, thermal resistance.

Part A of the Code makes it clear that in many cases there are alternative approaches to specification. The checklists may contain items which are considered to be alternatives in the context of the particular project.

The degree of detail to be given against each item is at the discretion of the designer. Items which do not apply to the particular project should, of course, be disregarded. Conversely, if the project design calls for important specification information not covered by the checklists, this should be provided.

Only the more common types of building and services work are included in this first edition of the Code. For work sections for which there are no checklists it is recommended that project specifications follow the scope of the appropriate sections of CAWS. This will avoid overlapping with other work sections and ensure co-ordination with the bills of quantities.

The checklists for engineering services, with minor exceptions, have been based on the technical content of the National Engineering Specification (NES). All other checklists have been based on the technical content of the National Building Specification (NBS). The sub-headings, sequence of items and terminology are not necessarily the same as in NES and NBS. Grateful acknowledgement is made to both NES Ltd and NBS Ltd.

*or specification preambles – see section 1.2.

A Preliminaries/General conditions

A10
Project particulars

Title and nature of project and postal address *

Names, postal addresses and telephone numbers of parties involved in the construction of the project and its administration:
   Employer *
   Project manager *
   Architect or Supervising Officer *
   Quantity Surveyor *
   Structural Engineer *
   Mechanical Engineer *
   Electrical Engineer *
   Landscape Architect *
   Resident Engineer
   Clerk of Works
   Main Contractor (sub-contract preliminaries only, if his identity is known)

A11
Drawings

Titles, identification numbers and scales of drawings prepared by the Employer's professional advisers as follows:
   Contract/Sub-contract drawings
   Drawings included with the tender documents
   Drawings from which the Bills of Quantities have been prepared *

Details of where and when drawings additional to those provided with the tender documents may be inspected *

(For conditions relating to the provision, use and interpretation of drawings see section A31)

A12
The site/Existing buildings

Details of the site for the Works, either by brief description or reference to relevant tender drawings, including:
   Topography, site boundaries, etc *
   Existing buildings on or adjacent to the site *
   Existing mains services *

How and when access may be obtained for inspection of the site and buildings *

Details of the ground conditions, types of soil, water table, either by description or reference to records of site investigation included with the tender documents *

Details of pre-contract work which has been, is being or will be carried out by others, including:
   Demolition and site clearance
   Ground stabilisation
   Other earthworks
   Foundation work

(For sectional possession of the site, restricted working area, restricted access see section A35)

A13
Description of the work

Outline description of the main materials, methods of construction and building services, either by description or reference to relevant tender drawings *

Dimensions and shape relating to each building *

Details of related work by others*

(For design constraints, sequence of construction, working hours, sectional completion see section A35)

A20
The Contract/Sub-contract

Schedule of clause headings of standard Conditions of Contract or Sub-contract with full text of any amendments or special conditions *

Full text of insertions to be made in any Appendix or Schedule to the Contract or Sub-contract *

Details of any additional requirements for the execution or enforcement of the Contract or Sub-contract eg:
   Executed under hand or seal*
   Performance guarantee bond *

Details of any Employer/Sub-contractor agreement(s)

(For additional Employer's requirements which are not to be incorporated as amendments or additions to the Contract itself see sections A30-A37)

* Detailed rules included in SMM7

40

A30
Employer's requirements:
Tendering/Sub-letting/Supply

Conditions for tender additional to those stated on the invitation to tender and/or form of tender, including:

Tendering procedure (by reference to standard Code of Procedure)

Visiting site before tendering

Period of validity of tenders

Alterations and qualifications to tender documents

Basis for pricing where quantities are given and SMM does not apply

Status of unpriced items

Procedure for dealing with errors and discrepancies

Conditions relating to sub-contracting or sub-sub-contracting:
    Named sub-contractors
    Listed firms
    Approved firms

Conditions relating to supply of goods

Requirements for submitting priced bills/schedules/specifications, programmes, method statements, etc at time of tender or shortly thereafter

Notification of sub-contract work for which the Main Contractor desires to tender

A31
Employer's requirements:
Provision, content and use of documents

Documents provided by the Employer's advisers:

Explanation of arrangement of documents

Description of system for recording issue of drawings

Obtaining additional copies

Interpretation generally, including:
    Definitions of terms and symbols used
    Definition of dates and amendments of British Standards and other documents referred to
    Requirements for documents to be read together

Limitations on use of dimensions taken from drawings

Limitations on use of bills of quantities for ordering

Procedure for dealing with discrepancies

(For lists of tender, contract and bill drawings see section A11)

Documents to be provided by the Contractor or Sub-contractor:

Programmes for preparation and issue

Procedures for inspecting, checking, amending and issuing

Timing of preparation and issue of documents

Manufacturer's technical literature

A32
Employer's requirements:
Management of the Works

Generally

Managment of the works, including all sub-contractors, suppliers, statutory authorities and others

Co-operation of sub-contractors with main contractor and others

Arrangements for site meetings/sub-contractor's meetings

Records of climatic and other conditions

Providing evidence of required insurances

Procedure when grounds for an insurance claim arise

Control of time

Preparing, submitting and monitoring programmes

Timing of ordering materials

Progress records, photographs, etc

Giving notice of start and completion of work

Avoiding or minimising delays due to adverse weather

Applications for extensions of time

Claims for disturbance of progress

Organising the works for phased completion or partial possession

Control of cost

Prior agreement of extent of renewal and repair work to existing buildings

Submission of cash flow forecasts

Submission of information relating to fluctuations

Submission of information relating to interim valuations

Disclosure of reservation of title

Giving notice before covering up work to be measured

Submission of daywork vouchers

Labour and plant records

A33
Employer's requirements: Quality standards/control

Standards of materials and work

Samples of products and work - definitions and procedures

Tests and samples additional to those specified (provisional sum(s))

Approval of products and work - definitions

Compliance with recognised good practice

Compliance with manufacturer's recommendations

Compliance with regulations of local authorities and statutory authorities

Ordering and supplying materials:
    Minimum quality
    Alternative sources
    Changes in product specifications

Handling, storing and fixing

Setting out, accuracy of the building as a whole and its parts

Procedure in case of non-compliance

Notification of defects in existing work

Supervision/Inspection

Delegation of Architect's powers

Resident Engineer - functions and powers

Clerk of Works - functions and powers

Amount and quality of Contractor's/Sub-contractor's supervision

Access for inspecting the work

Covering up completed work

Inspection of work executed during overtime

Contractor's/Sub-contractor's quality assurance systems

Test certificates

Completion/Making good defects

Arrangements for opening up and remedying defective work

Completing, cleaning and making good the building

Commissioning of systems

Adoption of roads, etc by the Local Authority

A34
Employer's requirements: Security/Safety/Protection

General requirements for security of the works during construction and at completion *

Ensuring the stability of the works

Prevention of nuisance and danger to persons, including those using or gaining access to adjacent occupied premises

Protection and making good of:
    Live services *
    Public and private roads and footpaths *
    Soft landscape
    Existing site features
    Adjoining buildings and contents*

Protection against:
    Explosion
    Fire
    Storm and surface water
    Inclement weather
    Accumulation of rubbish
    Pollution and hazardous substances *
    Radio/TV interference
    Laser equipment
    Noise: *
        Plant generally
        Cutting tools
        Operatives' radios

Protection of the works, including work in all sections*

(For specific protective works or facilities required by the Employer see section A36)

A35
Employer's requirements: Specific limitations on method/ sequence/timing

(The requirements given in this section will be supplementary to limitations described or implicit in information given elsewhere, eg sections A32, A33, A34, A36)

Sectional possession of the site (if not covered by Appendix to Contract)

Restrictions on working area

Restrictions on access including temporary openings *

Design constraints *

Method and sequence of construction *

Limitations on start of work *

Limitations on working hours *

Sectional completion or partial possession (if not covered by Appendix to Contract)

Restrictions on use of the site, eg advertising *

Use or disposal of materials *

* Detailed rules included in SMM7

A36
Employer's requirements: Facilities/Temporary works/ Services

Accommodation for the Architect, Quantity Surveyor, Clerk of Works, etc:
    Offices *
    Sanitary accommodation*

Accommodation for site meetings *

Rates, services, cleaning, etc in connection with offices and accommodation *

Temporary fences, screens, hoardings, roofs, etc *

Name boards *

Telephone installation and rental*

Facsimile installation, rental and maintenance*

Telephone/facsimile call charges*

Special lighting

Temperature and humidity levels, other requirements for drying out *

Surveying and other equipment *

Employer's requirements regarding facilities, temporary works and services, required by the Contractor for his own use, eg:
    Location of huts, spoil heaps, etc
    Removing temporary works on completion
    Reading meters for apportioned cost of services

(For facilities, temporary works, temporary services, etc not specifically required by the Employer but neverthless provided by the contractor see A4)

A37
Employer's requirements: Operation/Maintenance of the finished building

Facilities and services required to be provided by the Contractor/Sub-contractor at Completion or thereafter to help the Employer operate and maintain the finished building, including:
    Product guarantees
    Lists of spares to be stocked
    Supply of spares
    Operation and maintenance manuals
    Training of Employer's staff
    Maintenance to be carried out
    Repair services to be available

(For facilities and services required by the Employer during construction see section A36)

(For work to complete the building and making good defects see most sections, but particularly Quality standards/ control, A33)

A40-A44
Contractor's general cost items

Items provided in bills of quantities as a check list for tenderers and for convenience in pricing. The items generally are implicit in the contract and as such are at the discretion and risk of the contractor. The list of items given in the project bills will not necessarily cover every type of cost incurred by the Contractor, and he may add other items at his discretion.

The headings are for no purpose other than pricing. They should not be used for specifying Employer's requirements - CAWS sections A30 to A37 inclusive should be used for this purpose.

This being so, it may be asked why sections A40 - A44 'Contractor's general cost items' are included in the set of specification checklists at all. They have been included for the convenience of practitioners, for without them Preliminaries/ General conditions would have been incomplete.

A40
Contractor's general cost items: Management and staff

Management and other staff *

A41
Contractor's general cost items: Site accommodation

Site accommodation*

---

* Detailed rules included in SMM7

A42
Contractor's general cost items: Services and facilities

Power *
Lighting *
Fuels for: *
   Drying out
   Testing and commissioning
Water *
Telephone and administration *
Measures for safety, health and welfare *
Storage of materials *
Rubbish disposal *
Cleaning *
Facilities for drying out *
Measures for protection of work in all sections *
Measures for security *
Maintaining public and private roads *
Small plant and tools *
General attendance on nominated sub-contractors* (for special attendance see A51)
Other attendant labour *

A43
Contractor's general cost items: Mechanical plant

Cranes *
Hoists *
Personnel transport *
Other transport *
Earthmoving plant *
Concrete plant *
Piling plant *
Paving and surfacing plant *
Other mechanical plant *

A44
Contractor's general cost items: Temporary works

Temporary roads *
Temporary walkways *
Access scaffolding *
Support scaffolding and propping *
Hoardings, fans, fencing, etc*
Hardstanding *
Measures for compliance with traffic regulations *
Other temporary works *

A50
Work/Materials by the Employer

Details of work by persons engaged directly by the Employer *
Attendance on such persons*
Procedures in respect of components and materials provided by or on behalf of the Employer (details of each component/ material being given in the relevant work section) *

A51
Nominated sub-contractors

Sums for and descriptions of work to be carried out by nominated sub-contractors, including details of drawings, programme, etc *
Items for Main Contractor's profit *
Items describing special attendance *
(For work to be carried out by 'Named' sub-contractors see relevant sections)

A52
Nominated suppliers

Sums for and descriptions of goods to be obtained from nominated suppliers *
Items for Main Contractor's profit *
(For fixing of goods see relevant sections)

A53
Work by statutory authorities

Sums for work by:
   The Local Authority *
   Statutory undertakings *
Items describing special attendance

A54
Provisional work

Sums for work and facilities which, at the time of tender, are not fully or firmly decided*
(For provisional sum for tests and samples additional to those specified see section A33)
(For provisional sum for telephone calls on behalf of the Employer see section A36)

A55
Dayworks

Sums for labour, materials and plant to be provided and paid for on daywork *
Definition of methods of determining value

* Detailed rules included in SMM7

44

C Demolition/Alteration/ Renovation

C41
Chemical dpcs to existing walls

Description of building, particularly areas affected by dpc work

Requirements for the Contractor to survey the building, ascertain condition and report on recommended measures

Identity of proprietary dpc system

Local removal of internal and/or external finishes

Position/level of dpc in relation to ground and floor levels

Drilling and making good holes

Making good to finishes if and to the extent included in this section

Builder's work to be carried out by others, including making good to finishes .

Guarantees and maintenace instructions

C52
Fungus/Beetle eradication

Scope and nature of the work

Description of building and nature of attack

Requirements for the Contractor to survey the building and submit proposals for:
  Eradication treatment, with quantities
  Builders work

Designer's specific requirements for treatment:
  Location and extent
  Preservative
  Method of application

General technical requirements

Details of special environmental conditions to be maintained

Propping, screening, protecting, etc

Limitations on access and working hours

Cutting out, removing and disposing of existing material

Preservation of existing materials and fabric

Drying out

Cleaning

Treatment of:
  Dry rot
  Wet rot
  Insect infestation

Treatment by:
  Brush/Spray application
  Injection
  Mayonnaise paste
  Irrigation
  Insecticidal smoke

Guarantees/Maintenance instructions

D Groundwork

D20
Excavating and filling

General information and requirements

Description of the work where not evident from the drawings

Site investigation report

Soils and strata, known and/or to be assumed for tender purposes

Details of existing services

Removal of trees, undergrowth, site features, cultivated turf, etc

Excavating

Restrictions on use of materials arising from the excavations

Prior treatment with herbicide

Excavating topsoil

Restrictions on sequence to maintain stability

Benching of gradients to receive filling

Accuracy of excavated formation levels

Timing of exposure, inspection and sealing of formations

Procedure if exposed formations are not satisfactory

Provision of earthwork support

Procedure if sides of excavations are dangerously unstable

Breaking out/removing/re-filling old foundations, beds, basements, tanks, etc

Breaking out or sealing off or diverting existing drains, waterways, etc

Hazardous/toxic substances

Historical/archaelogical remains

Backfilling of excavations taken wider or deeper than required

Disposal or storage of surplus excavated material

Topsoil spoil heaps:
    Maximum height
    Treatment with herbicide
    Covering

Keeping excavations free from water

Disposal of water

Filling

Condition of excavations at time of filling

Restrictions on cold weather working

General requirements for fill material:
    Consistency in any one layer
    Moisture content limits

Definition of selected excavated material

Type(s) of imported material, source(s), grading(s), soluble sulphate content, etc:
    Soil
    Rock
    Other hard fill/hardcore
    Graded granular material

Requirements for compaction:
    Maximum depth of layer
    Type of plant
    Minimum number of passes

Accuracy of filled formation levels

Protection of surface of filled areas

Blinding with fine material

E In situ concrete/Large precast concrete

E10
In situ concrete

General requirements for concrete mixes

Chloride content

Sulphate content

Quality of aggregates generally

Water absorption of aggregates

Drying shrinkage of aggregates

Mechanical properties of aggregates

Aggregates for exposed work

Aggregates prone to alkali-silica reaction

Conditions for use of ready mixed concrete

Storage of materials

Testing of materials

Submission of evidence of suitability of mixes

Batching and mixing requirements

Testing of concrete:
    Laboratory
    Content of test reports
    Maintenance of complete records
    Early age strength testing
    Procedure in the event of test failures

Requirements for each concrete mix

For designed mixes:
    Grade
    Permissible cements
    Permissible aggregates
    Nominal maximum size of aggregate
    Minimum cement content
    Maximum free-water cement ratio
    Maximum cement content
    Admixture and dosage
    Testing

For ordinary prescribed mixes:
    Grade
    Permissible cements
    Permissible aggregates
    Nominal maximum size of aggregate

For special prescribed mixes:
    Permissible cements
    Permissible aggregates
    Nominal maximum size of aggregate
    Mix proportions
    Workability
    Admixture and dosage
    Composition testing

General requirements for construction

Underlays to prevent premature loss of water

Placing and compacting requirements, including limitations on timing, sequence, speed of pouring, size of bays

Special precautions during cold or very hot weather

Re-vibrating to remove plastic settlement cracking

Construction joints:
    Limitations on location
    Treatment of faces

Curing and protecting requirements

Watertightness, including any special measures eg investigation of leaks, pressure grouting

Testing of completed work for structural adequacy, watertightness, etc

E20
Formwork for in situ concrete

General requirements

Accuracy, tolerances, including top surfaces

Cambers in beams and slabs

Stability, including loads to be accommodated

Propping and prop bearings

Forming of joints, holes, chases, inserts (also limitations on cutting)

Coffer and trough units

Form ties, making good tie holes

Release agents, surface retarders

Work below ground, including casting against faces of excavations

Preparation of structural steelwork before encasing in concrete

Striking, removing props

Permanent formwork/form linings

For structural reinforcement:
    Ribbed steel mesh
    Profiled steel sheets

For insulation:
    Sheet materials against or in lieu of formwork
    Sheet materials against ground formation

For visual effect:
    Sheet materials
    Bricks
    Tiles

For other purposes:
    Expanded steel mesh (for mechanical key)
    Collapsible boards (for clay heave conditions)
    Under-slab damp proof membrane

Formed concrete finishes

Type of formwork/form lining and its size/arrangement/jointing

Limitations on irregularities, colour variation, projecting fins, blowholes

Limitations on use and type of cover spacers

Limitations on use of form ties, their type , location and making good

Treatment at arrisses and other features

Requirements/limitations for making good

Provision of samples for approval

Requirements for special protection

E30
Reinforcement for in situ concrete

Type and grade of bar reinforcement

Type and designation of fabric reinforcement

Protective coatings (galvanizing, powder coating, etc)

Condition of reinforcement at time of placing concrete

Laps where not detailed

Measures to prevent rust staining

Cutting and bending (eg temperature, radii)

Fixing generally

Tying wire

Use of mechanical or welded joints

Cover:
    Tolerances
    Use of cover meters
    Type and spacing of spacers/chairs

E40
Designed joints in in situ concrete

Construction of formed joints

Treatment of joint faces

Joints in wearing surface floors

Construction of crack inducing joints

Bottom of slab inducers

Top of slab inserted inducers

Formed grooves

Cut grooves

Joint accessories

Waterstops and their installation

Tie bars, mesh tie strips

Dowel bars, debonding compound, compressible caps

Membranes for sliding joints

Sheet joint fillers

Gun grade sealants and their application (reference to section Z22)

Preformed sealants and their installation (reference to section Z22)

E41
Worked finishes/Cutting to in situ concrete

Special requirements for accuracy/tolerances on wet worked finishes

Vacuum dewatering

Working of surfaces:
  Brushing
  Tamping
  Floating
  Trowelling
  Applying non-slip grit
  Hacking
  Scoring
  Grinding
  Abrasive blasting
  Tooling
  Applying surface hardeners

Treatment at arrises and other features

Requirements/limitations for making good

Control samples

Requirements for special protection

Limitations on methods of cutting holes, grooves and chases

Grouting in bolts, etc

E50
Precast concrete large units

General information/requirements

General description of the work

Programme constraints

Where contractor design is required:
  Information to be submitted at tender stage
  Information to be submitted before manufacture

General requirements for concrete mixes (reference to section E10)

Tolerances/accuracy of units and assembled construction

Design, construction and maintenance of moulds

Type and designation of reinforcement

Concrete cover to reinforcement

Requirements/limitations on use of cover spacers

Casting, demoulding, curing

Production quality control, inspection and records

Handling, storing and protecting units

Procedure with damaged units

Provision of samples for approval

Erection

Requirements for each basic type of unit

Reference to related drawings

Identity of proprietary system, if any

Type(s) of unit:
  Structural frames
  Large panel wall/cladding units
  Floor and roof decks forming an integral part of the precast concrete structural assembly
  Stair flights, ramps
  Retaining wall units

Performance requirements:
  Floor loads
  Wind loads
  Other loads
  Deflection limits
  Weather resistance
  Thermal resistance
  Accommodation of thermal and moisture movements

Details of concrete mix (reference to section E10)

Details of finish:
  Formed
  Worked
  Cast-on material

Accessories/features/incorporated components

Types of fixing, type and grade of metal

Method of jointing, including materials:
  Mortars
  Sealants
  Baffles

F Masonry

F10
Brick/Block walling

General requirements

Materials storage and handling
Wetting of bricks/blocks
Bonding
Bedding
Overhand laying
Height of lifts
Accuracy and dimensions
Setting out
Levelling of separate leaves
Brickwork/blockwork for plastered finish
Fire stopping
Work during inclement weather
Mortar testing
Protection of the finished work

Additional requirements for facework

Control samples
Colour mixing
Appearance generally
Cutting
Bonding
Brick slips
Sills and cappings
Jointing and pointing
Cleanliness

Requirements for each type of walling

Brick/block:
    Standard designation
    Proprietary designation
    Compressive strength
    Finish/colour
    Work sizes
Special shapes
Mortar mix and colour (reference to section Z21)
Bond
Joint treatment
Special features (eg string courses, sills, thresholds, copings, steps, quoins, irregular angle corners, closures) requiring different bond or use of special shape bricks
Bonding to existing work

F20
Natural stone rubble walling

General requirements

Inspection of samples of stone
Evidence of skill of operatives
Control samples
Work during inclement weather
Laying and bonding of stones:
    Regularity of appearance
    Accuracy
    Cleanliness
Protection of the finished work

Requirements for each type of walling

Stone:
    Type and source
    Finish
    General quality
Mortar mix (reference to section Z21)
Coursing/bonding
Profile and finish to joints

F21
Natural stone ashlar walling/ dressings

General requirements

Preparation and checking of shop drawings
Inspection of samples of stone
Evidence of skill of operatives
Control samples
Cutting and dressing of stones
Arrangements for inspection at works
Work during inclement weather
Laying and bonding of stones:
    Size and regularity of joints
    Accuracy
    Cleanliness
Protection of the finished work

Requirements for each type of walling

Stone:
    Type and source
    Finish
    General quality
Mortar mix (reference to section Z21)
Bond
Joggles, dowels, etc
Fixing to backing wall with cramps, bonding, etc
Method of finishing joints, and profile
Dressings, eg cornices, string courses, quoins, panels
Other special features

F30
Accessories/Sundry items for brick/block/stone walling

Damp proof courses/cavity trays

Horizontal dpcs

Vertical dpcs

Jamb dpcs

Sill dpcs

Coping/capping dpcs

Cavity trays formed in situ

Preformed cavity trays

Cavity trays over openings

Dpc/Cavity tray junction cloaks

Dpcs in facework

Reinforcing/Fixing accessories

Wall ties and their spacing

Dovetail slot ties

Sliding anchors

Angle supports

Joint reinforcement, including bedding and laps

Special fixings

Cavities

Cleanliness

Weepholes

Rigid sheet cavity insulation, including size, thickness, fixing

Air bricks, ventilation gratings

Bridging ducts

Closers

Movement joints

Expansion joints

Contraction joints

Sealing of joints (reference to section Z22)

Proprietary sills, lintels, copings, dressings

Precast concrete

Prestressed concrete

Cast stone

Clayware

Natural stone (including slate)

Steel

Plastics

Miscellaneous items

Tile sills/creasing

Building in frames

Use of templates

Fixing bricks

Flue lining system

Flue blocks

Refuse chutes

Flue terminals

Stoves, grates, fire surrounds, hearths,

'Fix only' clauses for components and materials which are built into or onto the walling, but are not an integral part of it, eg:
Built-in windows and doors
Ends of joists and joist hangers
Holding down straps
Ends of floor and roof beams

F31
Precast concrete sills/lintels/copings/features

This section does not include:
Precast concrete large units
(See section E50)
Proprietary precast concrete sills, lintels, copings, etc.
(See Accessories/Sundry items for brick/block/stone walling, F30)

General requirements

General requirements for concrete mixes (reference to section E10)

Tolerances/accuracy of units and assembled construction

Design, construction and maintenance of moulds

Type and designation of reinforcement

Concrete cover to reinforcement

Requirements/limitations on use of cover spacers

Casting, demoulding, curing

Production quality control, inspection and records

Handling, storing and protecting units

Procedure with damaged units

Provision of samples for approval

Building into walling

Requirements for each basic type of unit

Type(s) of unit:
Lintels, sills, mullions and transomes, jambs
Copings and cornices
Pier and chimney caps
Finials, corbels, small panels, etc.
Tracery
Steps, landings
Handrails and cappings
Balustrades, balusters and newels
Corbels, templates and padstones

Details of concrete mix (see checklist for section E10)

Details of finish:
Formed
Worked
Cast-on material

For ordinary builder's lintels, in relation to the various spans:
Size of lintel
Length of bearing
Size and number of bars

G Structural/Carcassing metal/ timber

G10
Structural steel framing

General information/requirements for steelwork

General description of the work

Reference to related drawings

Programme constraints

Detailed design and shop drawings

Design parameters and constraints

Co-ordination with others

Builder's work

Materials for steelwork

Hot rolled steel

Cold formed steel

Profiled sheet for floor slabs

Bolt assemblies

Bolt boxes

Deformed rods

Fabrication and erection

General quality of work

Materials storage and handling

Marking of members

Shop assembly and inspection

Making good surface flaws and dressing welds

Welding:
    General quality
    Approval of procedures
    Approval of welders

Bolting

Submission of proposals for erection

Erection

Accuracy

Approval of site modifications

Movement joints

Column bases

Site inspection and testing

General requirements for protective coatings

(For decorative coatings applied at a later stage see section M60)

Coating materials generally

Delivery, storage and usage

Compatibility

Treatment of inaccessible surfaces

Blast cleaning

Sequence of blast cleaning/priming/fabrication

Manual cleaning

Preparation for welding of painted steelwork

Treatment of site welded joints

Treatment of bolted joints

Treatment of friction grip joints

Preparation and painting of bolts

Painting:
    Suitability of conditions
    Application
    Measurement of wet and dry film thicknesses

Handling, storing and protecting coated steelwork

Remedial work to defective coatings

Requirements for each type of coating

Galvanizing:
    Preparation
    Minimum average coating thickness

Painting (in each case state shop or site):
    Preparation
    Primer and dry film thickness
    Intermediate coat and dry film thickness
    Stripe coats
    Top coat, dry film thickness and colour

G20
Carpentry/Timber framing/First fixing

General requirements

Materials storage and handling

Stress grading:quality assurance

Moisture content

Processing treated timber

Dimensions of timbers

Selection and use of timber:
    Position of notches and holes
    Scarf joints, finger joints, splice plates
    Warping

General quality of jointing/fixing

Accuracy

Prototypes

Testing

Protection:
    Avoidance of over-stressing and distortion
    Maintenance of moisture content
    Sealing end grains
    Painting before delivery
    Blemishes on planed faces

Jointing:
    Nailed joints
    Screwed joints
    Framing anchors
    Metal plate fasteners/gussets
    Bolted joints
    Connectors
    Glued joints
    Anti corrosive finishes to fastenings

Joist hangers

Tie down straps

Lateral restraint straps

Erection

Temporary/permanent bracing/restraint

Requirements for each type of timber

Softwood/hardwood:
    Use/location
    Species, origin and stress grade
    Strength class
    General quality (if not graded)
    Surface finish
    Treatment

Plywood:
    Use/location
    National standard
    Type
    Grade
    Nominal thickness/number of plies
    Finish
    Treatment

Glued laminated timber:
    Manufacturing standard
    Species and origin
    Grade
    Adhesive type
    Surface classification
    Treatment
    Works applied finish

Trussed rafters:
    Manufacturing standard
    Types/weights of roof covering and ceiling
    Type of system
    Ancillary components
    Treatment

H   Cladding/Covering

H10
Patent glazing

General requirements

Where contractor design is required:
    Information to be submitted at tender stage
    Information to be submitted before construction

Tolerances/accuracy

Checking accuracy and general suitability of building structure

Performance requirements:
    Weather resistance
    Wind, snow and other loads

Storing, handling, cutting and fixing

Cleanliness, particularly of double glazing

Protection, freedom from defects

Requirements for each type of glazing

Details of supporting structure:
    Type and size of members
    Spacing
    Pitch

Patent glazing system, including:
    Type of bars - profile, material, finish
    Spacing of bars
    Bottom overhang/lap

Infill materials:
    Glass
    Plastics glass
    Insulating sealed glass units
    Panels

Accessories, eg:
    Opening lights
    Doors
    Louvres
    Vents
    Opening/Control gear
    Ironmongery
    Special weatherings
    Draught proofing

H13
Structural glass assemblies

General requirements

Where contractor design is required:
    Information to be submitted at tender stage
    Information to be submitted before construction

Tolerances/accuracy

Checking accuracy and suitability of structure

Performance requirements:
    Wind and other loads
    Weather resistance

Storing, handling and fixing

Applying sealants

Protection, cleaning, freedom from defects

Requirements for each type of glazing

Details of supporting structure

Type of glass, and edge treatment

Fixing/jointing:
    Glass to glass: mechanical fixings, sealants
    Glass to building fabric: channels, gaskets, etc

Fittings/accessories:
    Doors
    Rails
    Ironmongery

H21
Timber weatherboarding

General requirements

Materials storage and handling

Control sample

Moisture content

Finishing and protecting

Requirements for each type of weatherboarding

Supports and spacing (see section G20)

Breather paper/felt

Boards:
    Profile and size
    Species
    Surface class
    Preservative/flame retardant treatment

Fixing of boards

Type and location of heading joints

Cover beads and fillets

H30
Fibre cement profiled sheet cladding/covering/siding

General requirements

Provision of shop drawings and other information
Wind, snow and maintenance loads
Suitability of structure and work thereto
Materials storage and handling
Safety requirements
Laying and sealing vapour barriers
Fitting insulation
Cutting and drilling sheets
Setting out
Sequence of construction
Provision for thermal movement
Flashings and trims

Requirements for each type of sheeting

Pitch, spacing and nature of supports
Sheets:
    Type
    Profile
    Thickness/gauge
    Finish/colour
Primary fastenings:
    Type
    Number per sheet
End laps, sidelaps: size, sealing, fixing
Fastings, trims, filler pieces, spacers, tapes, sealant, etc
Insulation
Vapour barrier
Internal lining

Accessories/Features

Cavity barriers
Structural movement joints
Gutters and outlets
Eaves
Verges
Hips
Valleys
Abutments
Ridges
Junctions
Bottom edges
Angles
Skirtings
Rooflights
Ventilators
Profile fillers
Access warning notices

H31
Metal profiled/flat sheet cladding/covering/siding

General requirements

Provision of shop drawings and other information
Wind, snow and maintenance loads
Suitability of structure and work thereto
Materials storage and handling
Cutting and drilling sheets
Setting out
Sequence of construction
Provision for thermal movement
Flashings and trims

Requirements for each type of cladding

Pitch, spacing and nature of supports
Sheets of composite panels:
    Type
    Profile
    Thickness/gauge
    Finish/colour
Primary fastenings:
    Type
    Spacing
End laps, side laps: size, sealing, fixing
In double skin construction:
    Type of insulation, including spacers
    Vapour barrier, including lapping and sealing
    Internal lining, including jointing

Accessories/Features:

Cavity barriers
Structural movement joints
Gutters and outlets
Eaves
Verges
Hips
Valleys
Abutments
Ridges
Junctions
Bottom edges
Angles
Skirtings
Rooflights
Ventilators
Profile fillers
Access warning notices

H41
Glass reinforced plastics cladding/features

General information/requirements

Where contractor design is required:
  Information to be submitted at tender stage
  Information to be submitted before production
Provision of samples, mock-ups, units for testing
Structural requirements, loadings, deflections
Colour fastness, resistance to change of translucency
Thickness of gel coats
Curing requirements, testing of hardness
Minimum weight of reinforcement
Minimum resin: glass ratio
Monitoring weight of units
Accuracy of units, setting out and erection
Maintenance of records
Restrictions on making good damage

Requirements for each type or application

Type of construction (single skin, sandwich, etc)
Finish and colour
U value
Fire rating
Type of fixings
Type of joints, baffles, sealants, etc
Accessories, features, incorporated components

H50
Precast concrete slab cladding/features

General requirements

Where contractor design is required:
  Information to be submitted at tender stage
  Information to be submitted before production
Tolerances/accuracy of cladding
Performance requirements:
  Wind and other loads
  Weather resistance
  Accommodation of thermal and moisture movements
Casting, demoulding, curing
Handling, storing and protecting units
Fixing methods and procedures
Control samples

Requirements for each type of cladding

Details of concrete mix (See checklist for section E10)
Details of finish:
  Formed
  Worked
  Cast-on material
Types of fixing, type and grade of metal
Width and filling for basic joints
Width and filling for movement joints
Cavity insulation
Accessories (copings, cills, dpcs, flashings, etc)

H51
Natural stone slab cladding/features

General requirements

Where contractor design is required:
  Information to be submitted at tender stage
  Information to be submitted before production
Tolerances/accuracy of cladding
Performance requirements:
  Wind and other loads
  Weather resistance
  Accommodation of thermal and moisture movements
Selection of stone for freedom from defects
Cutting of stone:
  Minimum thicknesses
  Accuracy
  Stones left oversize for cutting on site
Handling, storing and protecting stone
Fixing methods and procedures
Control samples

Requirements for each type of cladding

Type and source of stone, and finish
Types of fixing, type and grade of metal
Width and filling for basic joints
Width and filling for movement joints
Cavity insulation
Accessories (copings, cills, dpcs, flashings, etc)

H52
Cast stone slab cladding/features

General requirements

Where contractor design is required:
  Information to be submitted at tender stage
  Information to be submitted before production
Tolerance accuracy of cladding
Performance requirements:
  Wind and other loads
  Weather resistance
  Accommodation of thermal and moisture movements
Casting, demoulding, curing
Handling, storing and protecting units
Fixing methods and procedures
Control samples

Requirements for each type of cladding

Details of cast stone mix:
  Minimum cement content
  Compressive strength
  Drying shrinkage
  Initial surface absorption
Types of fixing, type and grade of metal
Width and filling for basic joints
Width and filling for movement joints
Cavity insulation
Accessories (copings, cills, dpcs, flashings, etc)

H60
Clay/Concrete roof tiling

General requirements

Storing, handling and fixing

Mortar mixes (reference to section Z21)

Battens:
    Quality of timber
    Limitations on length
    Limitations on incidence of joints
    Fixing

Underlay:
    Direction
    Size of laps
    Fixing, avoidance of tears and ponding

Requirements for each type of tiling

Base:
    Vertical or sloping (give pitch)
    Rafters or studs (give centres)
    Solid backgrounds - masonry/sheathing

Type of tile

Fixing - nailing/clipping:
    General areas
    Local areas

Head/End laps

Battens/Counterbattens:
    Size(s)
    Preservative treatment

Underlay, insulated or plain

Accessories/Features

Eaves

Vertical bottom edges

Vertical angles:
    Internal
    External

Abutments:
    Sloping
    Vertical
    Top courses

Verges

Hips, hip irons

Valleys:
    Swept
    Laced
    Sheet metal gutter
    Preformed gutter

Party walls

Ridges

Special junctions

Vents

Finials

Pipe slates

Sheet undercloaks

H61
Fibre cement slating

General requirements

Storing, handling and fixing

Mortar mixes (reference to section Z21)

Battens:
    Quality of timber
    Limitations on length
    Limitations on incidence of joints
    Fixing

Underlay:
    Direction
    Size of laps
    Fixing, avoidance of tears and ponding

Requirements for each type of slating

Base:
    Vertical or sloping (give pitch)
    Rafters or studs (give centres)
    Solid backgrounds - masonry/sheathing

Type of slate

Fixing method and laps

Battens/Counterbattens:
    Size(s)
    Preservative treatment

Underlay, insulated or plain

Accessories/Features

Eaves

Vertical bottom edges

Vertical angles:
    Internal
    External

Abutments:
    Sloping
    Vertical
    Top courses

Verges

Hips:
    Close mitred
    With ridge tiles, hip irons

Valleys:
    Close mitred
    Sheet metal gutter
    Preformed gutter

Party walls

Ridges

Special junctions

Vents

Finials

Pipe slates

Sheet undercloaks

H62
Natural slating

General requirements

Storing, handling and fixing

Mortar mixes (reference to section Z21)

Battens:
    Quality of timber
    Limitations on length
    Limitations on incidence of joints
    Fixing

Underlay:
    Direction, size of laps
    Fixing, avoidance of tears and ponding

Requirements for each type of slating

Base:
    Vertical or sloping (give pitch)
    Rafters or studs (give centres)
    Solid backgrounds - masonry/sheathing

Type of slate

Type of slating:
    Uniform length, random width:
        Length
        Minimum width
        Minimum end lap
        Minimum side lap
    Uniform length and width:
        Size
        Minimum end lap
        Half lap bonding
    Random widths in diminishing courses:
        Maximum/minimum length
        Widths related to lengths
        Minimum end lap
        Maximum deviation of joints from centres of slates in course below

Battens/counterbattens:
    Size(s)
    Preservative treatment

Underlay, insulated or plain

Accessories/Features

Eaves

Vertical bottom edges

Vertical angles:
    Internal
    External

Abutments:
    Sloping
    Vertical
    Top courses

Verges

Hips:
    Close mitred
    With ridge tiles, hip irons

Valleys:
    Swept
    Laced
    Sheet metal gutter
    Preformed gutter

Party walls

Ridges

Special junctions

Vents

Finials

Pipe slates

Sheet undercloaks

H71
Lead sheet coverings/flashings

General requirements:

Limitations on laying including protection of bases

General integrity of construction, including:
    Watertightness
    Freedom of thermal movement
    Adequacy of fixings

Removing existing lead:
    To be property of Contractor - credit
    To remain property of Employer - weighing, storage

Checking suitability of base

Preparation of existing timber bases:
    Making good
    Plywood underlayment

Timber for rolls, fillets, etc:
    General quality
    Moisture content
    Preservative treatment

General quality of lead

Dimensions and details of various types of joint:
    Wood cored rolls
    Hollow rolls
    Welted
    Standing seams
    Capped battens
    Recessed
    Laps/overlaps
    Drips

Intermediate fixings:
    Face (dot)
    Hidden (tack)

Forming of details:
    Bossing
    Leadburning

Fixings for clips and heads of sheets:
    Nailing to timber
    Screwing to concrete and brick

Wedging into joints and chases

Dimensions and detail of clips:
    Lead
    Copper
    Stainless steel

Sacrificial sheets in particular locations

Plaques

Applying patination oil

Requirements for each type of covering/flashing

Roofing/wall cladding:
    Base material and condition
    Preparation/making good to existing bases
    Underlay
    Lead code and type:
        Milled
        Machine cast
        Sand cast
    Longitudinal joints:
        Type
        Spacing
        Eaves detail
    Cross joints:
        Type
        Spacing
    Intermediate fixings
    Ridge/Hip/Head detail

Lead covered cladding panels:
    Core
    Lead code and type
    Longitudinal joints and spacing
    Cross joints and spacing
    Intermediate fixings for lead
    Method of fixing panels

Dormers:
  Base material and condition
  Preparation
  Underlay
  Lead code and type
  Joints on top and sill
  Joints on cheeks
  Intermediate fixings
Gutters:
  Base material and condition
  Preparation
  Underlay
  Lead code and type
  Longitudinal joints, if any
  Cross joints and spacing
  Fixing at sides
  Outlets
Flashings:
  Type(eg step, apron, cover)
  Lead code and type
  Clip fixings and spacing
  Spacing and size of lap joint
  Lap with material being flashed
  Fixing into joints/chases
Soakers:
  Lead code
  Length, underlaps
  Fixing
Weatherings:
  Base material
  Preparation
  Underlay
  Lead code and type
  Fixings and spacings
  Type and spacing of joints
  Edge details
Ridge/Hip rolls:
  Clips and spacing
  Timber core and fixings
  Lead code
  Spacing and size of lap joints
  Head nailing to hip iron

J Waterproofing

J20
Mastic asphalt tanking/damp proof membranes

General requirements

Checking suitability of background/base
Ground de-watering
Watertightness and general integrity of construction
Application generally
Treatment of joints, angles, edges
Treatment at pipes and pipe sleeve/penetrations
Covering with permanent overlying construction

Requirements for each type of tanking/dpm

Base material and condition
Location:
    Basement floor
    Basement walls
    Ground floor
Preparation:
    Keying to concrete
    Keying to brickwork
    Keying to blockwork
    Isolating membrane
Type of asphalt
Number of coats and nominal thickness

J21
Mastic asphalt roofing/insulation/finishes

General requirements

Checking suitability of base
Materials storage and handling
Limitations on laying including protection of moisture absorbent bases/insulation
Watertightness and general integrity of construction
Application generally
Application to vertical and sloping surfaces
Treatment of joints, angles, edges
Treatment at pipes and pipe sleeves
Completion including testing drainage falls
Protection

Requirements for each type of roofing

Cold roofs:
    Base material and condition
    Preparation, including any keying treatment, primer or isolating membrane
    Type of asphalt, number of coats and nominal thickness
    Finish, e.g. rubbed, solar reflective paint, chippings, tiles
Warm roofs:
    Base material and condition
    Preparation, including any keying treatment or primer
    Vapour barrier and bonding/fixing
    Insulation type, thickness and bonding/fixing
    Isolating membrane
    Type of asphalt, number of coats and nominal thickness
    Finish, e.g. rubbed, solar reflective paint, chippings, tiles
Inverted roofs:
    Base material and condition
    Preparation, including any keying treatment, primer or isolating membrane
    Type of asphalt, number of coats and nominal thickness
    External insulation and bonding if any
    Ballast or finish

Accessories/Features

Pressure release vents
Edge trims

J30
Liquid applied tanking/damp proof membranes

General requirements

Checking suitability of base/background
Materials storage and handling
Watertightness and general integrity of construction
Application of cold/hot applied coatings

Requirements for each type of tanking/dpm

Base material and condition
Location:
   Basement floor
   Basement walls
   Ground floor
Preparation including primer
Type of coating, number of coats and coverage
Reinforcement at angles, joints, pipes, etc.
Blinding/Protection

J40
Flexible sheet tanking/damp proof membranes

General requirements

Checking suitability of background/base
Ground dewatering
Watertightness and general integrity of construction
Fillets and reinforcement strips at angles
Junctions with dpcs
Treatment at pipe, duct and cable penetrations
Protective screeds and walls
Covering with permanent overlying construction
Protecting tanking with impregnated fibreboard to prevent damage by backfilling

Requirements for each type of tanking/dpm

Oversite membrane:
   Blinding layer to hardcore
   Sheet material, number of layers
   Jointing
   Thickness and mix of protective concrete layer
Underslab dpm:
   Blinding layer to hardcore
   Sheet material, number of layers
   Jointing
Loose laid overslab dpm:
   Sheet material, number of layers
   Laps, method of bonding
   Full bonding to sloping/vertical surfaces
Fully bonded dpm/tanking:
   Sheet material, number of layers
   Primer
   Laps
   Bonding (self-adhesive, torch on or hot compound)

J41
Built up felt roof coverings

General requirements

Materials storage and handling
Limitations on laying including protection of moisture absorbent bases/insulation
Watertightness and general integrity of construction
Checking suitability of base
Use of mechanical stripping:
   Chippings
   Chippings and felt
Making good:
   Blisters, splits
   Levelling ponded areas
   Patching
Treatment at joints in base
Priming/bonding compounds
Method of bonding/fixing felt:
   Full (pour and roll or torch on)
   Partial (Strip, frame or spot)
   Partial (Venting base layer)
   Nailing
Supplementary requirements for metal faced felt
Treatment at joints, angles, edges
Treatment at pipes and pipe sleeves
Treatment at outlets
Completion, including testing drainage falls
Protection, including restrictions on traffic and following trades

Requirements for each type of roof covering

New cold roofs/Renewal of existing felt:
   Base material and condition
   Preparation:
      Stripping (if applicable)
      Making good
      Items to be removed/refixed
      Primer
   Waterproof membrane:
      Standard or system reference
      First layer and bonding
      Intermediate layer and bonding
      Top layer and bonding
   Surface protection:
      Chippings
      Tiles
      Solar reflective paint
Warm roofs on new decks/existing felt:
   Base material and condition
   Preparation:
      Stripping (if applicable)
      Patching, repairing, making good
      Items to be removed/refixed
      Primer
   Vapour barrier and bonding
   Insulation type, thickness and bonding/fixing
   Waterproof membrane:
      Standard or system reference
      First layer and bonding
      Intermediate layer and bonding
      Top layer and bonding
   Surface protection:
      Chippings
      Tiles
      Solar reflective paint
Inverted roofs on new decks/existing felt:
   Base material and condition
   Preparation:
      Stripping (if applicable)
      Patching, repairing, making good
      Items to be removed/re-fixed

Waterproof membrane:
    Standard or system reference
    First layer and bonding
    Intermediate layer and bonding
    Top layer and bonding
Insulation:
    Type and thickness
    Bonding/fixing
Surface protection:
    Filter membrane
    Ballast
    Paving slabs and supports

Accessories/Features

Pressure release vents

Edge trims

Fillets

Pressed metal skirtings

Movement joints and cappings

K Linings/Sheathing/Dry partitioning

K10
Plasterboard dry lining

General requirements

Materials, storage and handling
Control samples
Preparation of background
Additional supports
Limitations on working
Jointing and finishing

Requirements for each type of lining

Background
Board type and size
Method of fixing and fixing centres:
    Nailing/screwing to timber studs/joists
    Screwing to metal furrings
    Pad and dab
    Adhesive
Jointing and finishing
Other requirements, e.g. vapour barrier

K11
Rigid sheet flooring/sheathing/linings/casings

General requirements

Materials storage, handling and conditioning
Setting out
Additional supports
Cutting holes
Limitations on working
Finishing, protecting

Requirements for each type of flooring/sheathing/lining/casing

Background/supports and spacing (see section G20)
Sheet type and size
Preservative/Flame retardant treatment
Layout, e.g:
    Direction of long edges
    Joints staggered/in line
Method of fixing and fixing centres:
    Nails
    Screws
    Adhesive
Joint treatment:
    Tight butt
    Gap
    Filled
    Chamfered
    Cover sections/trims

Accessories/Features

Access panels
Cavity barriers (may be included in section P12)

K12
Under purlin/Inside rail panel linings

General requirements

Materials storage and handling
Setting out
Limitations on working
Protection

Requirements for each lining system

Panel type and size
Support system
Thermal insulation material and thickness

Accessories/Features

Access panels
Cavity barriers (may be included in section P10)

K13
Rigid sheet fine linings/panelling

General requirements

Provision of shop drawings

Materials storage, handling and conditioning

Moisture content

Limitations on working, including environmental conditions

Control samples/mock ups

Fabrication:
    Site dimensions
    Accuracy
    General quality of manufacture
    Laminating, veneering
    Lippings, edgings, arrisses

Fixing door frames

Hanging doors

Fixing and adjusting ironmongery

Protection

Requirements for each type of lining/panelling

Background

Battens:
    Size
    Spacing
    Fixing

Panels:
    Core
    Veneer
    Edge treatment/jointing
    Finish
    Fixing

Door frames:
    Material
    Finish
    Fixing

Door leaves:
    Thickness
    Core
    Veneer
    Lipping
    Finish
    Furniture and ironmongery

Access panels:
    Core
    Veneer
    Lipping
    Finish
    Accessories

K20
Timber board flooring/ sheathing/linings/casings

General requirements

Materials storage and handling

Moisture content

Limitations on working, including environmental conditions

Finishing and protecting

Requirements for each type of flooring/ sheathing/lining/casing

Supports and spacing (see section G20)

Boards:
    Profile and size
    Species
    Surface class
    Preservative/Flame retardant treatment

Method of fixing

Type and location of heading joints

K21
Timber narrow strip flooring/ linings

General requirements

Materials storage, handling and conditioning

Moisture content

Control samples

Limitations on working, including environmental conditions

Protection

Requirements for each type of flooring/lining

Base/background

Battens:
    Size
    Preservative/Flame retardant treatment

Fixing of battens:
    Nailed
    Screwed
    Adhesive
    Plain clips
    Spring clips

Resilient layer

Insulation

Strips:
    Profile and size
    Species
    Surface class
    Fire retardant treatment

Fixing of strips

Type and location of heading joints

Special features:
    Margins
    Expansion joints
    Sanding, sealing, polishing

K31
Plasterboard fixed partitions/inner walls/linings

General requirements

Materials storage and handling

Control sample

Limitations on working

Setting out

Quality, thickness and finish of steel for studs, channels and furrings

Quality of timber for framing, battens, noggings, head and sole plates

Cavity barriers

Workmanship generally:
Fixing framing
Fixing panels
Joints between panels

Repairing damage to panels

Surface coating to receive paint or wall covering

Requirements for each type of partition/inner wall/lining

Stud partitioning:
Nominal thickness of partition and height
Stud centres
Boards/panels
Finish, e.g. taped seamless
Other requirements, e.g. treatment at edges, acoustic quilt

Laminated partitions:
Nominal thickness of partition and height
Core material and thickness
Outer layers material and thickness
Finish, e.g. open joints for plastic compound by others

Wallboard panel partitioning:
Standard/proprietary reference of panels
Nominal thickness and height
Finish, e.g. taped seamless
Other requirements, e.g. acoustic sealant to perimeter battens

Dry lining on metal furrings:
Background
Nominal thickness of lining and height
Fixing of furrings
Boards
Fixing of boards to furrings
Finish

K40
Suspended ceilings

General requirements

Contractor to provide detailed design/co-ordination/installation drawings and other information

Co-ordination with others

Materials storage, handling and conditioning

Control samples

Limitations on working conditions

Setting out, including procedure for dealing with irregular spaces

Levels and allowable deflection

Fixings and fastenings

Fire resisting ceilings:
Accommodating expansion
Sealing gaps at service penetrations and edges

Protection

Requirements for each type of ceiling

Type of ceiling (proprietary description)

Membrane:
Material and type (tile, board, panel, strip)
Size and thickness
Finish/texture
Fire rating

Suspension system:
Nominal depth of void
Grid type and size
Exposed/concealed
Finish
Hanger type and spacing
Fire rating

Accessories/features:
Access panels
Ventilation slots/grilles
Integral fittings/service outlets
Cavity fire barriers
Reveals to rooflights and changes in level
Perimeter trims

L Windows/Doors/Stairs

L10, L11, L12
Windows/Rooflights/Screens/Louvres

General requirements

Provision of shop drawings

Provision of evidence of performance

Protection and storage

Fixings and fastenings

Protection against contact with aggressive/incompatible materials

Sealing ends/priming before delivery

Use of approved/licensed installers

Adjustments for correct operation

Windows/Roof windows/Sub-frames

Clauses for each separate type of window according to:
  Type:
    Side hung
    Top hung
    Horizontal pivot
    Vertical pivot
    Horizontal sliding
    Vertical sliding
    Louvre
    Fixed
    Other
  Material:
    Timber
    Steel
    Aluminium
    UPVC
    Composite
  Type of specification:
    British or Trade Standard
    Performance
    Proprietary
    Purpose made
For each of the above clauses, detailed requirements as relevant:
  Proprietary or Standard reference
  Drawing reference
  Performance requirements:
    Standard reference
    Exposure category
    Design wind pressure
    Air permeability test pressure class
    Watertightness test pressure class
    Wind resistance test pressure class
    Operation and strength characteristics
  Reference to sections Z10 or Z11
  Timber:
    Species and class
    Moisture content
    Preservative treatment
  Adhesive
  Glazing details:
    Factory glazed
    Site glazed (reference to section L40)
  Finish as delivered:
    Standard/proprietary
    Primed/painted (reference to section Z30)
  Weatherstripping
  Accessories:
    Shutters
    Sills
    Architraves/trims

    Mechanical/automatic operating equipment
  Ironmongery
  Installation:
    Built in/prepared openings
    Fixing
  Sealing:
    Sealant
    Sealing strips
    Reference to section Z22

Other components

Timber screens/louvres/doors:
  Proprietary reference
  Drawing reference
  Reference to section Z10
  Timber:
    Species and class
    Moisture content
    Preservative/fire retardant treatment
  Adhesive
  Glazing details (reference to section L40)
  Finish as delivered (reference to section Z30)
  Ironmongery/accessories
  Installation
Metal screens/louvres/doors:
  Proprietary reference
  Drawing reference
  Reference to section Z11
  Material:
    Steel
    Aluminium
    Other
  Glazing details (reference to section L40)
  Louvre details:
    Single/double/triple banked blades
    No through vision
  Finish as delivered
  Ironmongery/accessories
  Installation
Rooflights:
  Proprietary reference
  Drawing reference
  Upstand:
    Material
    Ventilation
    Fixing
  Domelight/skylight:
    Material
    Fixing

L20, L21, L22
Doors/Shutters/Hatches

General requirements

Provision of shop drawings

Provision of evidence of performance

Protection and storage

Fixings and fastenings

Protection against contact with aggressive/incompatible materials

Sealing ends/priming before delivery

Use of approved/licensed installers

Adjustments for correct operations

Door leaves

Clauses for each separate type of door accoding to:
  Material:
    Timber
    Aluminium
    Plastics
    Rubber
    All glass
  Type of specification:
    British Standard
    Proprietary
    Purpose made
  Performance/location:
    Internal
    External
    Fire resisting
  Style:
    Matchboard
    Panel
    Flush painted
    Flush veneered
  Operation:
    Hinged/Pivotted
    Sliding
For each of the above clauses, detailed requirements as relevant:
  Proprietary or Standard reference
  Drawing reference
  Reference to sections Z10 or Z11
  Timber species and class
  Core, facings, lippings
  Moisture content
  Preservative/fire retardant treatment
  Adhesive
  Glazing details.
    Factory glazed
    Site glazed (reference to section L40)
  Finish (reference to section Z30)
  Special features

Frames/linings

Clauses for each type of frame/lining according to:
  Material:
    Timber
    Pressed steel
  Type of specification:
    British Standard
    Proprietary
    Purpose made
  Performance/location:
    Internal
    External
For each of the above clauses, detailed requirements as relevant:
  Proprietary or Standard reference
  Drawing reference
  Reference to sections Z10 or Z11
  Timber species and class
Moisture content
Preservative/Fire retardant treatment
Adhesive
Architraves/trims
Finish (reference to section Z30)
Special features:
  Weather stripping
  Intumescent strips
Installation:
  Built in/prepared openings
  Fixing
  Bedding/pointing (reference to section Z22)

Door leaves/hatches and surrounds

Clauses for each type of component/assembly according to:
  Type:
    Door sets
    Patio doors
    Hatches
    Other
  Material:
    Timber
    Aluminium
    Plastics
    Glass
    Other
    Composite
  Type of specification:
    British Standard
    Proprietary
    Purpose made
  Performance/location:
    Internal
    External
    Fire resisting
    Acoustic
    Security
For each of the above clauses, detailed requirements as relevant:
  Proprietary or Standard reference
  Drawing reference
  Reference to sections Z10 or Z11
  Timber species and class
  Core, facings, lippings
  Moisture content
  Preservative/fire retardant treatment
  Adhesive
  Glazing details
  Factory glazed
  Site glazed (reference to section L40)
  Architraves/trims
  Finish (reference to section Z30)
  Ironmongery
  Special features:
    Weather stripping
    Intumescent strips
  Installation:
    Built in/prepared openings
    Fixing
    Bedding/pointing (refer to section Z22)

Special operation doors/shutters/grilles/ partitions

Clauses for each type, e.g.
  Rolling shutters
  Rolling grilles
  Collapsible gates
  Sliding/folding doors/partitions
  Up and over doors
  Revolving doors
  Automatic doors
  Strong room doors
For each of the above clauses, detailed requirements as relevant:
  Proprietary reference
  Material
  Finish
  Incorporated features
  Frames and guides
  Ironmongery
  Operating mechanism
  Incorporation into surrounding construction

67

L30, L31
Stairs/Walkways/Balustrades

General requirements
Provision of shop drawings
Protection and storage
Fixings and fastenings
Installation

Components
Purpose made timber stairs/walkways/balustrades:
    Type (straight flight, dog leg, etc)
    Standard reference
    Drawing reference
    Reference to section Z10
    Timber species, grade and class
    Moisture content
    Preservative/fire retardant treatment
    Adhesive
    Finish as delivered to site (reference to section Z30)
Purpose made metal stairs/walkways/balustrades:
    Type (straight flight, dog leg, spiral, etc)
    Drawing reference
    Reference to section Z11
    Material (steel, aluminium, stainless steel clad steel, etc)
    Finish as delivered to site (reference to section Z30)
Proprietary stairs/balustrades:
    Type (straight flight, spiral, etc)
    Material (steel, precast concrete, etc)
    Proprietary reference and specification options
Proprietary ladders:
    Type (access, companion way, loft)
Proprietary reference and specification options

L40
General glazing

General requirements
Quality of glass
Limitations on pre-glazing
Preparation of surrounds
Storing, handling, cutting, fixing
Edge cover and clearance
Setting blocks, distance pieces
Fixing of beads
Protection, cleaning, freedom from defects

Requirements for each type of glazing
Type of glass/glass unit/other pane material
Special treatment/working of glass, e.g.
    Surface treatment
    Edge treatment
    Curved

Surround, including any priming or sealing
Priming by glazier
Method of glazing, type and grade of materials:
    Putty fronting
    Bead:
        Compound bedding
        Tape and capping sealant
        Drained and ventilated
        Internal tape
        Type of bead and fixing
    Heel bead:
        Compound bedding
        Tape and capping sealant
        Sealant tape
        Internal trim
        Type of bead and fixing
    Groove:
        Compound bedding
        Tape and sealant
        Gasket
    Glass to glass:
        Sealant
        Gasket
    Mirror glazing:
        Dome top screws
        Adhesive pads
    Other types:
        Fire resistant channels
        Single sided gaskets

M Surface finishes

M10
Sand cement/Concrete/ Granolithic screeds/flooring

General requirements

Materials storage, sampling, testing
Batching, mixing, sampling, testing of mixes
Preparation of bases including minor repairs
Placing and compacting
Control samples
Limitations on working, e.g. in adverse weather
Contraction, daywork joints
Surface tolerances
Forming vertical surfaces (skirtings, risers)
Curing and protecting

Requirements for each type of screed/flooring

Type of construction/preparation of base:
    Monolithic
    Bonded
    Partially bonded
    Unbonded
    Floating
Insulating layer
Reinforcement
Limitations on bay size
Nominal thickness:
    Overall
    Surfacing mix if any
Details of proprietary mix
Details of non-proprietary mix:
    Permissible cements
    Permissible aggregates
    Grading limits of fine aggregate
    Nominal maximum size of coarse aggregate (if any)
    Maximum drying shrinkage
    Mix proportions
    Admixture
Sand-cement surfacing mix to no-fines or unbound dry screeds
Finish:
    Trowelled
    Trowelled dewatered
    Trowelled non-slip
    Floated
    Tamped
    Brushed
    Power ground
    Subsequent application of hardener or sealer

Accessories/Features

Cast-in elements, including pipes, conduits, heating cables
Movement joints:
    Preformed sections
    Metal edgings
    Sealants

M11
Mastic asphalt flooring

General requirements

Checking suitability of base
Materials handling
Limitations on laying
Limitations on remelting
Bay joints
Margins and skirtings.
Surface tolerance
Work to manholes, gullies, pipes
Curing and protecting

Requirements for each type of flooring

Type of base and preparation required
Type of construction:
    Bonded
    Separating layer
Grade, composition, colour of asphalt
Number of coats and nominal thickness
Type of surface finish:
    Matt
    Polished
    Crimped
    To receive another finish (state)

M20
Plastered/Rendered/Roughcast coatings

General requirements

Materials storage, sampling, testing
Batching, mixing, sampling, testing of mixes
Control samples
Preparation of backgrounds including minor repairs
Dubbing out
Limitations on working, e.g. in adverse weather
Drying/shrinkage time between coats
Surface tolerance
Curing and protecting

Requirements for each type of coating

Background
Preparation of background, including bonding treatment
Plaster baseboard, lath, plank, etc. if any
Number of coats and nominal thickness
Details of plaster mixes:
    Undercoat(s)
    Final coat
Details of proprietary render mix
Details of non-proprietary render mix:
    Permissible cements
    Permissible aggregates
    Grading limits of fine aggregate
    Nominal maximum size of coarse aggregate
    Mix proportions
    Admixtures
Surface finish:
    Trowelled smooth
    Stippled
    Combed
    Wood floated
    Scraped
    Roughcast
    Dry dash

Accessories/Features

Precast elements
Local reinforcement and fixing
Expansion and contraction joints
Beads, stops

M30
Metal mesh lathing/Anchored reinforcement for plastered coatings

General requirements

Materials storage and handling
Cutting and bending
Contractor's proposals for support systems/fixing methods
Limitations on working

Requirements for each type of lathing/reinforcement

Type of coating to be reinforced/supported (reference to M20)
Type of lathing/reinforcement:
    Plain
    Ribbed expanded metal
    Welded mesh
    Twisted wire netting
Material:
    Mild steel
    Galvanized steel
    Stainless steel
    Aluminium
Background/structure to which supports are fixed
Building paper for external lathing
Support system including hangers, spacers, runners, bearers
Spiral wrapping, stirrups, bandings for casings
Fixing/tying
Joints between sheets
Access panels

M40
Stone/Concrete/Quarry/Ceramic tiling/Mosaic

General requirements

Sequence/timing

Materials storage, sampling, testing

Preparation of backgrounds/bases including minor repairs

Keying/bonding treatments

Mortar for bedding (reference to section Z21):
  Permissible sands and grading limits
  Batching, mixing

Setting out

Control samples

Limitations on working, including in adverse weather

Surface tolerance

Curing and protecting

Requirements for each type of tiling/mosaic

Location:
  Wall/floor
  Internal/external

Type of tile/mosaic and size

Preparation of background/base

Method and thickness of adhesive bedding to walls/floors:
  Thin bed, ribbed/solid
  Thick bed

Adhesive for bedding

Method and thickness of mortar bedding to walls/floors:
  Bonded
  Separating layer

Mortar mix for bedding

Grouting material:
  Proprietary type
  Cement:sand
  Cement:lime:sand
  Pigments

Joint width

Accessories/Features

Movement joints:
  Preformed sections
  Sealants
  Metal edgings
Dividing strips

M41
Terrazzo tiling/In situ terrazzo

General requirements

Materials storage, sampling, testing

Preparation of bases including minor repairs

Mortar for bedding (reference to section Z21):
  Permissible cements
  Permissible sands and grading limits
  Batching, mixing

Setting out

Control samples

Limitations on working, including in adverse weather

Surface tolerance

Curing and protecting

Requirements for each type of terrazzo

Terrazzo tiling:
  Type of tile and size
  Preparation of base
  Bedding:
    Mix
    Nominal thickness
    Method of laying
  Laying tiles, including joint material and width
  Finishing:
    Grinding
    As laid
In situ terrazzo:
  Preparation of base
  Topping:
    Mix (proprietary reference or details of aggregate, size, grading, proportions)
    Nominal thickness
    Method of laying
  Bedding:
    Mix
    Nominal thickness
    Method of laying
  Dividing strips
  Finishing:
    Grinding
    Application of hardener
Precast terrazzo units:
  Type of unit and size
  Bedding and fixing

Accessories/Features

Movement joints:
  Preformed sections
  Metal edgings
  Sealants
Anti-static flooring:
  Location
  Details of construction
  Testing

M50
Rubber/Plastics/Cork/Lino/Carpet tiling/sheeting

General requirements

Materials storage, handling and conditioning
Control samples
Consistency of colours
Setting out
Drying out of bases, environmental conditions generally
Checking suitability of bases
Removing existing finishes
Use of smoothing compound
Laying underlayments
Laying tiling/sheeting
Limitations on working
Cleaning, finishing and protecting
Testing anti-static flooring
Provision of additional material

Requirements for each type of tiling/sheeting

Tile/sheet sizes, colour/pattern
Special requirements for patterns, features, sheet sizes, location of joints, etc
Preparation of base
Underlayment
Adhesive
Seam welding/bonding for sheets
Finishing

Accessories/Features

Edgings, trims
Cover strips
Nosings

M51
Edge fixed carpeting

General requirements

Materials storage and handling
Control samples
Drying out of bases
Checking suitability of bases
Laying interlayments, underlays
Laying carpeting
Limitations on working
Cleaning and protecting
Provision of additional material

Requirements for each type of carpeting

Carpet type, colour, pattern, width
Special requirements for setting out of pattern, seams and cross-seams
Preparation of base
Interlayment, underlay
Method of seaming
Method of fixing

Accessories/Features

Edgings, trims
Cover strips
Nosings

M52
Decorative papers/fabrics

General requirements

Submission of samples for approval
Checking materials for colour match
Environmental and lighting conditions for storage and hanging
Checking condition of backgrounds and adjacent surfaces before hanging
Treatment of mould infected backgrounds
Fixtures to be removed before hanging and re-fixed afterwards
Setting out
Selection and use of adhesives
Selection and use of lining papers
Jointing, pattern matching
Spare rolls, supply of additional material

Requirements for each type of covering

Background:
  Description
  Preparation
  Priming or sizing
Covering material
Lining paper
Adhesive

M60
Painting/Clear finishing

General requirements

Restrictions on use of different colour batches

Checking compatibility of materials

Testing of viscosity, etc

Preparing sample areas for approval

Programming of required staged inspections

Moisture content of backgrounds

Preparation materials

Fixtures/ironmongery to be removed before coating and re-fixed afterwards

Restriction on methods of removing existing coatings

Preparation of existing coated surfaces generally

Removing efflorescence

Treatment of mould infected backgrounds

Treatment of alkali affected coatings and backgrounds

Environmental and lighting conditions

Application of coatings generally

Painting of concealed surfaces before fixing

Painting of putty

Cleaning existing gutters and other features

Requirements for each type of coating

Surface:
  Location
  Description

Preparation:
  Removing existing coatings
  Preparing/making good existing coatings
  Timber for painting
  Timber for clear coating
  Manual cleaning of steel
  Blast cleaning of steel
  Galvanized steel
  Aluminium
  UPVC
  Concrete
  Masonry
  Plaster
  Plasterboard

Initial coat(s)

Finishing coat(s)

N Furniture/Equipment

N13
Sanitary appliances/fittings

General requirements

Protection from damage and disfigurement

Checking that floors, walls, bearers, etc. to which appliances are to be fixed are adequate for the purpose

Setting out and co-ordination with positions of supply and drainage services

Fixings/fastenings

Jointing/bedding compounds

Fixing and jointing of taps, wastes and overflows

Requirements for each type of appliance/fitting

Appliances:
   Type and material/finish/colour
   Taps/water supply fittings
   Waste and trap
   Supports
   Overflow
   Other accessories

Cisterns (if any):
   Type, material and size
   Valve and float
   Operating mechanism
   Flush/overflow pipe
   Supports

Other features/accessories

Sealing joints to building fabric/finishes

P Building fabric sundries

P10
Sundry insulation/proofing work/ fire stops

Insulation

Type and thickness of sheet/quilt/mat insulation:
  Laid between joists
  Laid on netting across joists
  Fixed between rafters/studs
  Fixed to studs
  Suspended vertically in cavities

Type and thickness of loose fibre/granular insulation:
  Blown between joists
  Loose laid between joists

Eaves ventilators to existing roofs

Insulation to:
  Loft access hatches
  Water cisterns (if not included in relevant services sections)

Sand pugging between joists, including thickness

Checking general completeness, integrity, absence of cold bridges

Membranes

Type and grade of vapour check membrane(s)

Type and grade of breather membrane(s)

Installation:
  Fixing
  Lapping/taping of joints
  Sealing at pipe/duct penetrations
  Checking for and sealing perforations

Cavity barriers

Large cavity barriers:
  Suspended reinforced fibre mats
  Suspended intumescent coated foil mesh

Small cavity barriers:
  Polyethylene sleeved with flanges
  Wire reinforced mineral wool

Installation:
  Fixing
  Sealing at joints, intersections, adjacent construction
  Sealing around pipes, ducts, trusses, beams, etc.
  Checking general integrity and effectiveness against passage of fire/smoke

P11
Foamed/fibre/bead cavity wall insulation

Survey of existing walls, either:
  Carried out by Employer and made available, or
  To be carried out by Contractor

Remedial work, either:
  Included in tender, or
  To be carried out by others

Checking suitability of walls

Cavity fill material

Requirements for approval of installers

Cavity width

Sealing gaps and openings

Injection holes

Making good

Checking flues

Clearing away

Detailed records of the installation

Submission of certificates, records and guarantees

P20
Unframed isolated trims/ skirtings/sundry items

Trims/sundry items not included as accessories in other sections:
  Skirtings/picture rails/Architraves
  Cover fillets/stops/trims/beads/nosings
  Shelves/worktops
  Window boards
  Isolated handrails/grab rails
  Unframed pinboards
  Other

For each of the above items, detailed requirements as relevant:
  Proprietary or Standard reference
  Material
  Timber:
    Species and class
    Moisture content
    Treatment
  Finish as delivered
  Fixing

P30
Trenches/Pipeways/Pits for buried engineering services

General requirements

Setting out

Temporary markers

Excavating pits and trenches

Laying pipeducts

Draw ropes

Protection to pipeducts/services:
    Identification tapes
    Cover tiles
    Other protection

Backfilling trenches

Permanant markers

Requirements for each type of pipeduct

Pipeducts provided by utilities

Pipeducts provided by Contractor:
    Material
    Method of jointing
    Colour(s)
    Size(s)
    Bed/surround material and dimensions

Access/Inspection/Stopvalve chambers/drawpits

Traditionally constructed chambers:
    Internal size
    Base
    Walls
    Step irons
    Slab
    Access cover

Proprietary chambers

Backfilling temporary drawpits

P31
Holes/Chases/Covers/Supports for services

General requirements

Co-ordination with sub-contractors

Holes and chases

Restrictions on cutting, size and location of holes and chases in:
    In situ concrete
    Precast concrete
    Steelwork
    Masonry
    Timber
    Other materials

Preformed holes

Pipe sleeves:
    Material
    Installation
    Fire/water resisting stopping/sealing

Fire/water resisting barriers at multi-service penetrations

Covers and supports

Access/trench covers:
    Type
    Material
    Size
    Frame/support
    Fixing

Service supports:
    Type
    Material
    Fixing: cast in, built in, surface mounted

Q Paving/Planting/Fencing/ Site furniture

Q10
Stone/Concrete/Brick kerbs/edgings/channels

General requirements

Handling, storing and installing units

Method of cutting units

Keeping units clean and free from concrete and mortar

Restrictions on working during inclement weather

Concrete mix for foundations and haunching (reference to section E10)

Mortar mix for bedding and pointing (reference to section Z21)

Levels, alignment and falls

Requirements for each type of unit

Units:
    Type (kerbs/edgings/channels/etc)
    Material
    Size
    Finish/colour
    Special shapes

Joints:
    Width
    Open or mortar filled

Special requirements, eg:
    Kerb dowels and installation
    Haunching dowels and installation

Movement joints:
    Joint filler and building in
    Width
    Sealant and application

Q20
Hardcore/Granular/Cement bound bases/sub-bases to roads/pavings

Checking CBR of sub-grade

Treatment of sub-grade with herbicide

Restrictions on working during inclement weather

Compaction of sub-grade:
    For vehicular areas
    For pedestrian areas

Filter/separator membrane laid on sub-grade

Granular material:
    Type
    Grading
    Frost susceptibility

Cement bound material:
    Type (granular material or soil)
    Cement content
    Method of incorporating cement

Compaction:
    Maximum depth of layer
    Type of plant
    Minimum number of passes

Accuracy of finished levels

Protection of surface of base/sub-base

Blinding with fine material

Q22
Coated macadam/Asphalt roads/pavings

General requirements

Checking accuracy and suitability of sub-base and kerbs/edgings/channels

Restrictions on working during inclement weather

Accuracy of finished levels

Contractor's use of pavements:
    Restrictions on use
    Timing of laying of wearing course
    Protective treatment to roadbase/basecourse
    Remedial treatment to roadbase/basecourse

Cleaning and preparation of abutments

Requirements for each type of paving

Surface treatment (if any):
    Dressing and chippings
    Coated chippings
    Crimping roller

Wearing course material and thickness

Base course material and thickness

Combined basecourse/road base material and thickness

Roadbase material and thickness

Thickness of granular sub-base
(included in section Q10)

Accessories

Timber for edgings, preservative treatment

Q24
Interlocking brick/block roads/pavings

General requirements

Submission of samples for approval

Preparation of sample areas for approval

Checking adequacy and suitability of sub-base and edge restraints

Restrictions on working during inclement weather

Accuracy of finished levels

Laying bedding, type of sand, thickness

Laying blocks/pavers

Method of cutting blocks/pavers

Compacting and jointing, type of sand for jointing

Vibrating plate compactor

Remedial work, particularly:
    Settlement of blocks/pavers
    Settlement of jointing sand

Requirements for each type of paving

Blocks/Pavers:
    Material and type
    Size, thickness
    Specials
    Colour/pattern

Setting out, bond, special features

Thickness of granular sub-base
(Included in section Q10)

Q25
Slab/Brick/Sett/Cobble/pavings

General requirements

Submission of samples for approval

Preparation of sample areas for approval

Checking adequacy and suitability of sub-base and kerbs/edgings/channels

Restrictions on working during inclement weather

Accuracy of finished levels

Method of cutting slabs/bricks

Protection and curing

Requirements for each type of paving

Slabs/bricks/setts/cobbles:
    Material
    Size, thickness
    Specials
    Colour/finish

Setting out, bond, special features

Bedding:
    Solid or spot
    Sand, damp mortar, wet mortar (state mix)
    Thickness

Jointing - width and method:
    Sand
    Sifted soil
    Dry mortar
    Mortar jointing
    Mortar pointing
    Hot sealant

Mix and thickness of concrete base
(reference to section E10)

Thickness of granular sub-base
(included in section Q10)

Movement joints, if any:
    Sealant
    Width
    Location

Accessories

Tree grilles

Q30
Seeding/Turfing

General requirements/Preparatory work

Cultivating and fine grading

Levels

Application/incorporation of:
    Peat
    Manure
    Compost
    Mulch
    Fertiliser
    Soil ameliorants
    Herbicides

Edging strips for lawn areas

Provision of water

Liability for plant failures

Protection, including provision of fencing

Seeding

Seed mixture/supplier

Season for sowing

Weather conditions

Sowing rate

Hydro-seeding

Rolling

Application of herbicide

Turf edgings

Watering

First cut

Turfing

Storage

Turf supplier/quality

Season for turfing

Weather conditions

Laying and consolidating

Edge treatment

Slopes - temporary fixing

Joint treatment

Watering

First cut

Other work

Work to existing grassed areas

Mesh reinforcement

Maintenance and other work to be executed during the
Defects Liability Period

Replacement seeding/turfing

Q31
Planting

General requirements/Preparatory work

Prior reservation of plants/trees

Substitution of specified plants/trees

Storage of plants/trees

Planting season

Weather conditions

Setting out

Protecting existing grass, etc.

Cultivating and grading

Incorporation of fertilisers/ameliorants

Application of herbicides

Provision of water

Liability for plant failures

Protection, including provision of fences/wind breaks

Trees

General quality and source:
    Nursery stock
    Advanced nursery stock
    Semi-mature

Planting:
    Dimensions of pits
    Backfill material including fertilisers/ameliorants
    Root pruning
    Orientation and levels
    Watering in
    Mulching
    Labelling

Staking:
    Number
    Type and treatment
    Size and height
    Type of tie

Guying

Tree guards

Plants

General quality and source:
    Bulbs/corms/tubers
    Herbaceous plants
    Shrubs
    Shrubs for hedges
    Roses

Planting/transplanting:
    Size of holes
    Planting and backfilling
    Anti-dessicants
    Pruning
    Watering in
    Forking over
    Mulching
    Labelling

Supports for climbers

Fence supports for hedges

Planting naturalized bulbs

Other work

Work to existing trees/planted areas:
    Pruning
    Cleaning and weeding
    Cultivating
    Fertilising/mulching

Maintenance and other work to be executed during the
defects liability period

Checking condition of stakes/ties/guys

Q40
Fencing

General requirements

Setting out
Setting posts in concrete/earth
Driving posts
Fixing timber rails
Site cutting of timber
Concrete mixes (reference to section E10)
Fixings and fastenings

Requirements for each type of fencing

Type of fencing:
    Chain link
    Woven wire
    Strained wire
    Wooden post and rail
    Steel continuous bar
    Concrete post and rail
    Timber close boarded
    Cleft chestnut pale
    Wooden palisade
    Steel vertical bar
    Steel palisade
    Concrete palisade
    Woven wood
    Concrete post and panel
    Purpose made
Fence material and treatment:
    Mesh/wire
    Bars/boards/pales
    Rails/verticals
    Panels

Height
Details at top/bottom
Posts/struts:
    Type/material
    Treatment
    Centres
    Method of setting/driving
Other requirements

Requirements for gates:

Type and size
Materials and treatment
Fittings
Method of setting posts

Q50
Site/Street furniture/equipment

General requirements

Handling, storing and protecting components
Concrete mixes (reference to section E10)
Setting components in concrete
Accuracy of location and fixing
Building components into walling

Requirements for each type of furniture/equipment

Gates (when not part of fencing), including lifting barriers
Pedestrian and vehicle barriers and railings
Bollards (including removable and collapsible)
Prefabricated plant containers
Seats, benches, tables
Litter bins, grit bins, dust bins
Poster display units
Cycle stands
Flag staffs
Clothes drying fittings
Sculptures and other ornamental features
Sports and playground equipment
Other special purpose equipment occuring externally

R Disposal systems

R10
Rainwater pipework/gutters

General requirements

Requirements for the system in use:
  Completeness of discharge
  Watertightness
  Ease of cleaning
  Accommodation of movement

Fixing and jointing pipes/gutters generally

Testing:
  Freedom from obstruction
  Air or water pressure (internal pipework)
  Gutter leakage

Requirements for each type of pipework

Location

Pipe:
  Material
  Size
  Accessories

Rainwater outlets to flat roofs/parapet gutters

Method of jointing

Method of fixing

Connections to underground drainage

Requirements for each type of gutter

Gutter and fittings:
  Material and gauge
  Shape and size

Method of jointing

Method of fixing

R11
Foul drainage above ground

General requirements

Requirements for the system in use:
  Completeness of discharge
  Watertightness
  Air tightness
  Maintenance of water seals
  Access and ease of cleaning
  Accommodation of movement

Pipe routes

Fixing and jointing pipework generally

Connections between dissimilar pipe materials

Testing:
  Freedom from blockage
  Air pressure
  Siphonage and back pressure

Requirements for each type of pipework

Purpose/location

Pipe:
  Material
  Size
  Accessories

Method of jointing

Method of fixing

R12
Drainage below ground

General requirements

Checking levels and positions of existing manholes, etc.

Protecting and maintaining existing live drains

Sequence of working

Excavating:
    Width of trench
    Accuracy of line and level
    Nature of formation
    Removing surplus material

Bedding and jointing pipes

Provision for differential movement at junctions with structures, manholes, etc.

Pipe cross-overs

Trenches containing more than one pipe

Connections to sewers

Backfilling

Concrete fill to trenches in close proximity to foundations

Testing and inspection:
    Water
    Air
    TV
    Ovality

Cleaning out at completion

Requirements for each type of pipeline

Pipes, bends and junctions:
    Material
    Type/strength class
    Size(s)

Type of subsoil

Bedding class:
    Bedding material and thickness
    Haunching material and size
    Surround material and thickness
    Backfilling material
    Additional protection, e.g. paving slabs, coloured tapes

Features/accessories

Gullies and other terminal fittings

Brick manholes/chambers:
    Concrete base, mix type (reference to section E10)
    Brickwork type (reference to section F10)
    Step irons
    Concrete slab, mix type (reference to section E10)
    Reinforcement

Precast concrete manholes/chambers:
    In situ base, mix type (reference to section E10)
    Type of manhole
    Type of joints
    Concrete surround, if any

Plastics inspection chambers:
    Type
    Bedding
    Surround/backfilling
    Concrete collar, if any

Manhole covers and frames

Channels and benching

Soakaways

Septic tanks/Cesspool tanks

R13
Land drainage

General requirements

Checking positions and levels of existing drains, watercourses and other services

Protecting and maintaining flow of existing live drains, and connecting to new

Special precautions near to trees and hedges

Excavating for pipes:
    Keeping topsoil separate
    Accuracy of line and level
    Removing surplus material

Trenchless pipe laying

Laying pipes, forming junctions

Backfilling with filter material

Mole drains - suitability of soil, surface, plant and gradients

Requirements for each type of drain

Pipe drains:
    Type of pipe (perforated, porous, open jointed)
    Material
    Size
    Minimum depth to invert
    Jointing
    Pipe bedding
    Filter material

Mole drains:
    Diameter of channels
    Spacing of channels
    Minimum depth to invert

Rubble (French) drains:
    Dimensions of trench
    Fill material

Features/accessories

Inspection chambers and silt traps:
    Bases
    Precast chambers
    Brick chambers
    Cover slabs
    Access covers

Headwalls

Connections to sewers

Outlets to watercourses

R20
Sewage pumping

Refer to reference specification checklists

Y10	Pipelines
Y11	Pipeline ancillaries
Y20	Pumps
Y25	Cleaning and chemical treatment
Y51	Testing and commissioning of mechanical services
Y52	Vibration isolation mountings
Y53	Control components - mechanical
Y54	Identification - mechanical
Y90	Fixing to building fabric
Y91	Off site painting/Anti-corrosion treatments
Y92	Motor drives - electric

Products/Materials specific to this section

Pumping station

Ejector station

S   Piped supply systems

S10
Cold water

Refer to reference specification checklists

Y10   Pipelines
Y11   Pipeline ancillaries
Y20   Pumps
Y21   Water tanks/cisterns
Y24   Trace heating
Y25   Cleaning and chemical treatment
Y50   Thermal insulation
Y51   Testing and commissioning of mechanical services
Y52   Vibration isolation mountings
Y53   Control components - mechanical
Y54   Identification - mechanical
Y90   Fixing to building fabric
Y91   Off site painting/Anti-corrosion treatments
Y92   Motor drives - electric

Products/Materials specific to this section

Water meters

Workmanship specific to this section

Connections to taps and appliances

S11
Hot water

Refer to reference specification checklists

Y10   Pipelines
Y11   Pipeline ancillaries
Y20   Pumps
Y22   Heat exchangers
Y23   Storage cylinders/calorifiers
Y25   Cleaning and chemical treatment
Y51   Testing and commissioning of mechanical services
Y52   Vibration isolation mountings
Y53   Control components - mechanical
Y54   Identification - mechanical
Y90   Fixing to building fabric
Y91   Off site painting/Anti-corrosion treatments
Y92   Motor drives - electric

Products/Materials specific to this section

Heated towel rails
Local direct water heaters

Workmanship specific to this section

Heated towel rail installation
Connections to taps and appliances
Local water heater installation

S12
Hot and cold water (small scale)

General information/requirements

General description of the work
Programme constraints
Information to be submitted with tender
Detailed design:
    Storage capacity
    Heat source (reference to section T32 if relevant)
    Pipeline sizes
    Draw off requirements
Provision of drawings by Contractor
General quality of work:
    Compliance with standards
    Storing and fixing
    Corrosion resistant fixings
    Accessibility for maintenance
    Self purging
    Free draining
Electrical work in connection
Fuel for testing
Builder's work

Equipment

Hot water boiler/circulator
Instantaneous water heater(s)
Instantaneous shower unit(s)
Storage water heater(s)
Flue pipe, flue lining
Balanced flue terminal
Air supply to appliance including ductwork
Cistern(s) and insulation
Hot water storage cylinder and insulation
Combination unit and insulation
Unvented hot water storage and insulation
Immersion heater(s)
Water softener

Pipelines

Type of tube and standard:
    Copper
    Plastics coated copper
    Chromium plated copper
    Stainless steel
    Polyethylene
Methods of jointing:
    Generally
    To equipment and fittings
Fixing:
    Generally
    Thermal movement
    Type of supports and centres
    Spacing from walls, ceilings, etc.
Location of pipe runs
Insulation
Sundry pipelines and insulation:
    Gas supply
    Warning pipes to cisterns
    Vent pipes
    External supply pipelines
    Pipelines entering buildings
Masking plates
Pipe ducts

Controls

Timer(s)
Thermostat(s)
Valves/cocks
Flush control device(s)

Completion

Testing water pipelines
Disinfectation
Testing gas supply pipelines
Operating and maintenance instructions
Provision of tools
Labelling

S13
Pressurized water

Refer to reference specification checklists

Y10   Pipelines
Y11   Pipeline ancillaries
Y20   Pumps
Y21   Water tanks/cisterns
Y24   Trace heating
Y25   Cleaning and chemical treatment
Y50   Thermal insulation
Y51   Testing and commissioning of mechanical services
Y52   Vibration isolation mountings
Y53   Control components - mechanical
Y54   Identification - mechanical
Y90   Fixing to building fabric
Y91   Off site painting/Anti-corrosion treatments
Y92   Motor drives - electric

Products/Materials specific to this section

Pressurization expansion units
Pressure booster sets
Water meters

Workmanship specific to this section

Installation

S21
Swimming pool water treatment

Refer to reference specification checklists
Y10   Pipelines
Y11   Pipeline ancillaries
Y20   Pumps
Y21   Water tanks/cisterns
Y22   Heat exchangers
Y24   Trace heating
Y25   Cleaning and chemical treatment
Y50   Thermal insulation
Y51   Testing and commissioning of mechanical services
Y52   Vibration isolation mountings
Y53   Control components - mechanical
Y54   Identification - mechanical
Y90   Fixing to building fabric
Y91   Off site painting/Anti-corrosion treatments
Y92   Motor drives - electric

Products/Materials specific to this section
Filter vessels
Chemical storage vessels
Chemical dosing equipment
Puddle flanges
Ozone generation equipment
Ozone injection equipment
Deozoning vessels
Electrolytic chlorine ion generation equipment
Pool inlet jets
Scum channels
Perimeter draw-off grilles

S41
Fuel oil storage/distribution

Refer to reference specification checklists
Y10   Pipelines
Y11   Pipeline ancillaries
Y20   Pumps
Y24   Trace heating
Y25   Cleaning and chemical treatment
Y50   Thermal insulation
Y51   Testing and commissioning of mechanical services
Y52   Vibration isolation mountings
Y53   Control components - mechanical
Y54   Identification - mechanical
Y90   Fixing to building fabric
Y91   Off site painting/Anti-corrosion treatments
Y92   Motor drives - electric

Products/Materials specific to this section
Storage tanks and vessels
Integral tanks
Service tanks
Oil storage tanks
Heaters for oil storage tanks
Oil level indicators
Fire valves
Accessories
Monitoring equipment
Screen filters
Single filters
Dual filters
Cartridge type strainers
Y type strainers
Oil meters

Workmanship specific to this section
Installation of oil storage tanks
Installation of oil distribution systems

S60
Fire hose reels

Refer to reference specification checklists

Y10   Pipelines
Y11   Pipeline ancillaries
Y20   Pumps
Y24   Trace heating
Y25   Cleaning and chemical treatment
Y50   Thermal insulation
Y51   Testing and commissioning of mechanical services
Y52   Vibration isolation mountings
Y53   Control components - mechanical
Y54   Identification - mechanical
Y90   Fixing to building fabric
Y91   Off site painting/Anti-corrosion treatments
Y92   Motor drives - electric

Generally for this section

Fire authority requirements

Products/Materials specific to this section

Fire hose reels
Pressure booster sets

Workmanship specific to this section

Fixing
Isolation
Notices
Installation of booster sets

S61
Dry risers

Refer to reference specification checklists

Y10   Pipelines
Y11   Pipeline ancillaries
Y25   Cleaning and chemical treatment
Y51   Testing and commissioning of mechanical services
Y54   Identification - mechanical
Y90   Fixing to building fabric
Y91   Off site painting/Anti-corrosion treatments

Generally for this section

Fire authority requirements

Products/Materials specific to this section

Inlet breechings
Inlet box
Landing valves
Outlet boxes
Drain valves

Workmanship specific to this section:

Installation of dry risers
Bonding
Installation of inlet boxes

S62
Wet risers

Refer to reference specification checklists

Y10   Pipelines
Y11   Pipeline ancillaries
Y20   Pumps
Y24   Trace heating
Y25   Cleaning and chemical treatment
Y50   Thermal insulation
Y51   Testing and commissioning of mechanical services
Y52   Vibration isolation mountings
Y53   Control components - mechanical
Y54   Identification - mechanical
Y90   Fixing to building fabric
Y91   Off site painting/Anti-corrosion treatments

Generally for this section

Fire authority requirements

Products/Materials specific to this section

Landing valves
Outlet boxes
Fire hose reel pump set
Pressure vessel with diaphragm
Control panel
Flow switch
Interconnecting pipework

Workmanship specific to this section

Installation of wet risers

S63
Sprinklers

Refer to reference specification checklists

Y10   Pipelines
Y11   Pipeline ancillaries
Y20   Pumps
Y21   Water tanks/cisterns
Y24   Trace heating
Y25   Cleaning and chemical treatment
Y50   Thermal insulation
Y51   Testing and commissioning of mechanical services
Y52   Vibration isolation mountings
Y53   Control components - mechanical
Y54   Identification - mechanical
Y90   Fixing to building fabric
Y91   Off site painting/Anti-corrosion treatments

General for this section

Fire authority requirements

Products/Materials specific to this section

Reaction and control devices and alarms
Sprinkler heads
Internal combustion engine drive and fuel system

T Mechanical heating/ Cooling/Refrigeration systems

T10
Gas/Oil fired boilers

Refer to reference specification checklists

Y10   Pipelines
Y11   Pipeline ancillaries
Y20   Pumps
Y21   Water tanks/cisterns
Y24   Trace heating
Y25   Cleaning and chemical treatment
Y50   Thermal insulation
Y51   Testing and commissioning of mechanical services
Y52   Vibration isolation mountings
Y53   Control components - mechanical
Y54   Identification - mechanical
Y90   Fixing to building fabric
Y91   Off site painting/Anti-corrosion treatments
Y92   Motor drives - electric

Products/Materials specific to this section

Boilers:
    Material
    Type
    Performance
    Efficiency
Boiler mountings
Safety of gas fired hot water boilers
Safety devices for hot water systems
Boilerhouse instrumentation and controls
Gas burners
Oil burners
Dual fuel burners
Burner controls
Acoustic shroud to burner
Blow down valves - parallel slide type
Blow down tanks
Pressurization plant
Ventilation to boiler rooms
Chimneys and flues
Smoke alarms

Workmanship specific to this section

Maintenance records
Gas boiler installation
Oil fired boiler installation
Analysis of flue gases

T11
Coal fired boilers

Refer to reference specification checklists

Y10   Pipelines
Y11   Pipeline ancillaries
Y20   Pumps
Y21   Water tanks/cisterns
Y25   Cleaning and chemical treatment
Y50   Thermal insulation
Y51   Testing and commissioning of mechanical services
Y52   Vibration isolation mountings
Y53   Control components - mechanical
Y54   Identification - mechanical
Y90   Fixing to building fabric
Y91   Off site painting/Anti-corrosion treatments
Y92   Motor drives - electric

Products/Materials specific to this section

Boilers:
    Material
    Type
    Performance
    Efficiency
Boiler mountings
Safety devices for hot water systems
Boilerhouse instrumentation and controls
Solid fuel burning equipment
Burner control
Solid fuel storage
Solid fuel handling equipment
Ash handling and storage equipment
Grit arrestors
Blow down valves - parallel slide type
Blow down tanks
Pressurization plant
Ventilation to boiler rooms
Chimneys and flues
Smoke alarms

Workmanship specific to this section

Maintenance records
Installation of underfeed stokers
Installation of pressurization unit

T12
Electrode/Direct electric boilers

Refer to reference specification checklists

Y10   Pipelines
Y11   Pipeline ancillaries
Y20   Pumps
Y21   Water tanks/cisterns
Y25   Cleaning and chemical treatment
Y50   Thermal insulation
Y51   Testing and commissioning of mechanical services
Y52   Vibration isolation mountings
Y53   Control components - mechanical
Y54   Identification - mechanical
Y90   Fixing to building fabric
Y91   Off site painting/Anti-corrosion treatments
Y92   Motor drives - electric

Products/Materials specific to this section

Boilers:
   Type
   Standard
   Access
   Manholes
   Supports
   Marking
   Testing
   Inspection
Electric water heaters
Blow down valves - parallel slide type
Blow down tanks
Pressurization plant

Workmanship specific to this section

Maintenance records
Installation of pressurization unit

T13
Packaged steam generators

Refer to reference specification checklists

Y10   Pipelines
Y11   Pipeline ancillaries
Y20   Pumps
Y21   Water tanks/cisterns
Y25   Cleaning and chemical treatment
Y50   Thermal insulation
Y51   Testing and commissioning of mechanical services
Y52   Vibration isolation mountings
Y53   Control components - mechanical
Y54   Identification - mechanical
Y90   Fixing to building fabric
Y91   Off site painting/Anti-corrosion treatments
Y92   Motor drives - electric

Products/Materials specific to this section

Steam generator
Blow down valves - parallel slide type
Blow down tanks
Ventilation to boiler rooms
Chimneys and flues
Smoke alarms

Workmanship specific to this section

Maintenance records
Flues

T20
Primary heat distribution

Refer to reference specification checklists

Y10   Pipelines
Y11   Pipeline ancillaries
Y20   Pumps
Y21   Water tanks/cisterns
Y25   Cleaning and chemical treatment
Y50   Thermal insulation
Y51   Testing and commissioning of mechanical services
Y52   Vibration isolation mountings
Y53   Control components - mechanical
Y54   Identification - mechanical
Y90   Fixing to building fabric
Y91   Off site painting/Anti-corrosion treatments
Y92   Motor drives - electric

T30
Medium temperature hot water heating

Refer to reference specification checklists

Y10   Pipelines
Y11   Pipeline ancillaries
Y20   Pumps
Y21   Water tanks/cisterns
Y22   Heat exchangers
Y23   Cylinders/calorifiers
Y25   Cleaning and chemical treatment
Y50   Thermal insulation
Y51   Testing and commissioning of mechanical services
Y52   Vibration isolation mountings
Y53   Control components - mechanical
Y54   Identification - mechanical
Y90   Fixing to building fabric
Y91   Off site painting/Anti-corrosion treatments

Products/Materials specific to this section

Natural convector heaters
Fan convector heaters
Continuous natural convectors
Radiant panels
Radiant strip heating
Site dimensions
Testing at manufacturer's works

Workmanship specific to this section

Installation

T31
Low temperature hot water heating

Refer to reference specification checklists

Y10   Pipelines
Y11   Pipeline ancillaries
Y20   Pumps
Y21   Water tanks/cisterns
Y22   Heat exchangers
Y23   Storage cylinders/calorifiers
Y25   Cleaning and chemical treatment
Y50   Thermal insulation
Y51   Testing and commissioning of mechanical services
Y52   Vibration isolation mountings
Y53   Control components - mechanical
Y54   Identification - mechanical
Y90   Fixing to building fabric
Y91   Off site painting/Anti-corrosion treatments

Products/Materials specific to this section

Radiators:
  Material
  Type
  Generally
Natural convector heaters
Fan convector heaters
Continuous natural convectors
Radiant panels
Radiant strip heating
Towel rails
Embedded pipe coils
Heated ceiling panels
Site dimensions
Testing at manufacturer's works

Workmanship specific to this section

Installation
Isolation
Embedded pipe coils installation

T32
Low temperature hot water heating (small scale)

General information/requirements:

General description of the work
Programme constraints
Information to be submitted with tender
Detailed design:
    Internal and external air temperatures
    U values
    Water temperatures and velocity
    Hot water (reference to section S12)
    Temperature and time controls
Provision of drawings by Contractor
General quality of work:
    Compliance with Standards and Byelaws
    Storing and fixing
    Fixing
    Corrosion resistant fixings
    Accessibility for maintenance
    Self purging
    Free draining
Electrical work in connection
Fuel for testing
Builder's work

Equipment

Central heating boiler
Fire with back boilers
Flue pipe, flue lining
Insulated chimney
Balanced flue terminal
Air supply to boiler including ductwork
Fuel storage tank and service pipe
Feed and expansion cistern and insulation
Circulating pump(s)
Radiators
Towel warmer radiators
Convectors
Underfloor heating system

Pipelines

Type of tube and standard:
    Copper
    Plastics coated copper
Method of jointing:
    Generally
    To equipment and fittings
Fixing:
    Generally
    Thermal movement
    Types of support and centres
    Spacing from walls, ceilings, etc.
Location of pipe runs
Insulation
Sundry pipelines and insulation:
    Gas supply
    Warning pipes to cisterns
    Vent pipes
Masking plates
Pipe ducts

Controls

Programmer/timer
Thermostat(s)
Valves/cocks
Radiator valves

Completion

Testing and balancing
Testing gas supply pipelines
Operating and maintenance instructions
As installed drawings
Provision of tools
Labelling

T40
Warm air heating

Refer to reference specification checklists

Y10   Pipelines
Y11   Pipeline ancillaries
Y20   Pumps
Y22   Heat exchangers
Y25   Cleaning and chemical treatment
Y30   Air ductlines
Y31   Air ductline ancillaries
Y41   Fans
Y42   Air filtration
Y43   Heating/Cooling coils
Y44   Humidifiers
Y45   Silencers/Acoustic treatment
Y46   Grilles/Diffusers/Louvres
Y50   Thermal insulation
Y51   Testing and commissioning of mechanical services
Y52   Vibration isolation mountings
Y53   Control components - mechanical
Y54   Identification - mechanical
Y90   Fixing to building fabric
Y91   Off site painting/Anti-corrosion treatments

Products/Materials specific to this section

Warm air heating units

Workmanship specific to this section

Installation

T60
Central refrigeration plant

Refer to reference specification checklists

Y10   Pipelines
Y11   Pipeline ancillaries
Y20   Pumps
Y21   Water tanks/cistern
Y23   Cylinders/Calorifiers
Y24   Trace heating
Y25   Cleaning and chemical treatment
Y41   Fans
Y45   Silencers/Acoustic treatment
Y46   Grilles/Diffusers/Louvres
Y50   Thermal insulation
Y51   Testing and commissioning of mechanical services
Y52   Vibration isolation mountings
Y53   Local controls - mechanical
Y54   Identification - mechanical
Y90   Fixing to building fabric
Y91   Off site painting/Anti-corrosion treatments
Y92   Motor drives - electric

Products/Materials specific to this section

Water chillers
Water cooling towers
Water cooled condensing units
Condensors
Design
Specialist installation
Works inspection
Performance
Maintenance
Safety
Equipment

Workmanship specific to this section

Connections
Access
Cleansing

T61
Primary/Secondary cooling distribution

Refer to reference specification checklists

Y10   Pipelines
Y11   Pipeline ancillaries
Y20   Pumps
Y25   Cleaning and chemical treatment
Y43   Heating/Cooling coils
Y50   Thermal insulation
Y51   Testing and commissioning of mechanical services
Y52   Vibration isolation mountings
Y53   Control components - mechanical
Y54   Identification - mechanical
Y90   Fixing to building fabric
Y91   Off site painting/Anti-corrosion treatments
Y92   Motor drives - electric

U Ventilation/Air conditioning systems

U10
General supply/extract

Refer to reference specification checklists

Y30 Air ductlines
Y31 Air ductline ancillaries
Y41 Fans
Y42 Air filtration
Y43 Heating/Cooling coils
Y45 Silencers/Acoustic treatment
Y46 Grilles/Diffusers/Louvres
Y50 Thermal insulation
Y51 Testing and commissioning of mechanical services
Y52 Vibration isolation mountings
Y53 Control components - mechanical
Y54 Identification - mechanical
Y90 Fixing to building fabric
Y91 Off site painting/Anti-corrosion treatments
Y92 Motor drives - electric

U11
Toilet extract

Refer to reference specification checklists

Y30 Air ductlines
Y31 Air ductline ancillaries
Y41 Fans
Y45 Silencers/Acoustic treatment
Y46 Grilles/Diffusers/Louvres
Y50 Thermal insulation
Y51 Testing and commissioning of mechanical services
Y52 Vibration isolation mountings
Y53 Control components - mechanical
Y54 Identification - mechanical
Y90 Fixing to building fabric
Y91 Off site painting/Anti-corrosion treatments
Y92 Motor drives - electric

U12
Kitchen extract

Refer to reference specification checklists

Y30 Air ductlines
Y31 Air ductline ancillaries
Y41 Fans
Y42 Air filtration
Y45 Silencers/Acoustic treatment
Y46 Grilles/Diffusers/Louvres
Y50 Thermal insulation
Y51 Testing and commissioning of mechanical services
Y52 Vibration isolation mountings
Y53 Control components - mechanical
Y54 Identification - mechanical
Y90 Fixing to building fabric
Y91 Off site painting/Anti-corrosion treatments
Y92 Motor drives - electric

Products/Materials specific to this section

Kitchen canopies
Grease filters

Workmanship specific to this section

Grease filter installation

U31
VAV air conditioning

Refer to reference specification checklists

Y10 Pipelines
Y11 Pipeline ancillaries
Y20 Pumps
Y25 Cleaning and chemical treatment
Y30 Air ductlines
Y31 Air ductline ancillaries
Y41 Fans
Y42 Air filtration
Y43 Heating/Cooling coils
Y45 Silencers/Acoustic treatment
Y46 Grilles/Diffusers/Louvres
Y50 Thermal insulation
Y51 Testing and commissioning of mechanical services
Y52 Vibration isolation mountings
Y53 Control components - mechanical
Y54 Identification - mechanical
Y90 Fixing to building fabric
Y91 Off site painting/Anti-corrosion treatments

Products/Materials specific to this section

VAV terminal units

Workmanship specific to this section

Installation

U32
Dual duct air conditioning

Refer to reference specification checklists

Y10 Pipelines
Y11 Pipeline ancillaries
Y20 Pumps
Y25 Cleaning and chemical treatment
Y30 Air ductlines
Y31 Air ductline ancillaries
Y40 Air handling units
Y41 Fans
Y42 Air filtration
Y43 Heating/Cooling coils
H44 Humidifiers
Y45 Silencers/Acoustic treatment
Y46 Grilles/Diffusers/Louvres
Y50 Thermal insulation
Y51 Testing and commissioning of mechanical services
Y52 Vibration isolation mountings
Y53 Control components - mechanical
Y54 Identification - mechanical
Y90 Fixing to building fabric
Y91 Off site painting/Anti-corrosion treatments

Products/Materials specific to this section

Mixing/blending units

Workmanship specific to this section

Installation

U40
Induction air conditioning

Refer to reference specification checklists

Y10 Pipelines
Y11 Pipeline ancillaries
Y20 Pumps
Y25 Cleaning and chemical treatment
Y30 Air ductlines
Y31 Air ductline ancillaries
Y40 Air handling units
Y41 Fans
Y42 Air filtration
Y43 Heating/Cooling coils
H44 Humidifiers
Y45 Silencers/Acoustic treatment
Y46 Grilles/Diffusers/Louvres
Y50 Thermal insulation
Y51 Testing and commissioning of mechanical services
Y52 Vibration isolation mountings
Y53 Control components - mechanical
Y54 Identification - mechanical
Y90 Fixing to building fabric
Y91 Off site painting/Anti-corrosion treatments

Products/Materials specific to this section

Induction units
Induction unit components
Induction unit accessories

Workmanship specific to this section

Installation

U41
Fan coil air conditioning

Refer to reference specification checklists

Y10   Pipelines
Y11   Pipeline ancillaries
Y20   Pumps
Y30   Air ductlines
Y31   Air ductline ancillaries
Y40   Air handling units
Y41   Fans
Y42   Air filtration
Y43   Heating/Cooling coils
H44   Humidifiers
Y45   Silencers/Acoustic treatment
Y46   Grilles/Diffusers/Louvres
Y50   Thermal insulation
Y51   Testing and commissioning of mechanical services
Y52   Vibration isolation mountings
Y53   Local controls - mechanical
Y54   Identification - mechanical
Y90   Fixing to building fabric
Y91   Off site painting/Anti-corrosion treatments

Products/Materials specific to this section

Fan coil units
Fan coil unit components
Fan coil unit accessories

Workmanship specific to this section

Installation

U42
Terminal re-heat air conditioning

Refer to reference specification checklists

Y10   Pipelines
Y11   Pipeline ancillaries
Y20   Pumps
Y25   Cleaning and chemical treatment
Y30   Air ductlines
Y31   Air ductline ancillaries
Y40   Air handling units
Y41   Fans
Y42   Air filtration
Y43   Heating/Cooling coils
H44   Humidifiers
Y45   Silencers/Acoustic treatment
Y46   Grilles/Diffusers/Louvres
Y50   Thermal insulation
Y51   Testing and commissioning of mechanical services
Y52   Vibration isolation mountings
Y53   Control components - mechanical
Y54   Identification - mechanical
Y90   Fixing to building fabric
Y91   Off site painting/Anti-corrosion treatments

Products/materials specific to this section

Ductline mounted reheat batteries

Workmanship specific to this section

Installation

V Electrical supply/power/ lighting systems

V12
LV supply/public utility supply

Refer to reference specification checklists

Y60   Conduit and trunking
Y61   HV/LV cables and wiring
Y62   Busbar trunking
Y63   Support components - cable
Y71   LV switchgear and distribution boards
Y80   Earthing and bonding components
Y81   Testing and commissioning of electrical services
Y82   Identification - electrical
Y90   Fixing to building fabric
Y91   Off site painting/Anti-corrosion treatments

Products/Materials specific to this section

Fuse pillars
Heater
Base unit
Poles and accessories
Poles
Cross-arms
Insulators for bare conductors
Insulator fittings and pins for bare conductors
Cable terminations, joints and binders for bare conductors
Hooks for insulated cables
Cross-arm accessories
Stay wire assemblies
Anti-climbing devices

Workmanship specific to this section

Alignment of poles
Assembly
Earthing
Clearance heights

V20
LV distribution

Refer to reference specification checklists

Y60   Conduit and trunking
Y61   HV/LV cables and wiring
Y62   Busbar trunking
Y63   Support components - cable
Y71   LV switchgear and distribution boards
Y74   Accessories for electrical services
Y80   Earthing and bonding components
Y81   Testing and commissioning of electrical services
Y82   Identification - electrical
Y90   Fixing to building fabric

Products/Materials specific to this section

Fuse pillars
Heater
Base unit

V21
General lighting

Refer to reference specification checklists

Y60   Conduit and trunking
Y61   HV/LV cables and wiring
Y62   Busbar trunking
Y63   Support components - cable
Y73   Luminaires and lamps
Y74   Accessories for electrical services
Y80   Earthing and bonding components
Y81   Testing and commissioning of electrical services
Y82   Identification - electrical
Y90   Fixing to building fabric
Y91   Off site painting/Anti-corrosion treatments

Products/Materials specific to this section

Lighting control equipment

V40
Emergency lighting

Refer to reference specification checklists

Y60 Conduit and trunking
Y61 HV/LV cables and wiring
Y63 Support components - cable
Y71 LV switchgear and distribution boards
Y73 Luminaires and lamps
Y74 Accessories for electrical services
Y80 Earthing and bonding components
Y81 Testing and commissioning of electrical services
Y82 Identificaiton - electrical
Y90 Fixing to building fabric
Y91 Off site painting/Anti-corrosion treatments

Products/Materials specific to this section

Emergency lighting system
Illumination of signs
Lamps for emergency lighting
Self-contained emergency lighting luminaire system and equipment
Central battery equipment
Battery chargers
Mains frequency central inverters

Workmanship specific to this section

Installation
Self-contained luminaires
Equipment

V90
General lighting and power (small scale)

General information/requirements

General description of the work
Programme constraints
Information to be submitted with tender
Detailed design
Co-ordination with others
Compliance with regulations
Division into circuits
Inspection and testing
Builders work
Operating and maintenance instructions
As installed drawings

Requirements for specific parts of the installation

Arrangements for electricity supply
Switchgear
Distribution boards
Containment systems:
    Conduit
    Trunking
    Ducting
Cabling:
    Sizing
    Routes
Accessories:
    For power
    For lighting
    Luminaires, lamps
Other equipment to be connected
Earthing and bonding
Fire stopping
Identification

Other systems included

Emergency lighting:
    Category and duration
    Central battery system
    Luminaires
Fire alarm system:
    Control equipment
    Alarm sounders
    Call points
    Detectors
    Other requirements
Door control system:
    Entrance door panel
    Telephone units
    Lock release
    Accessories

W Communications/ Security/Control systems

W50
Fire detection and alarm

Refer to reference specification checklists

Y60   Conduit and trunking
Y61   HV/LV cables and wiring
Y63   Support components - cable
Y71   LV switchgear and distribution boards
Y74   Accessories for electrical services
Y80   Earthing and bonding components
Y81   Testing and commissioning of electrical services
Y82   Identification - electrical
Y90   Fixing to building fabric
Y91   Off site painting/Anti-corrosion treatments

Generally for this section

Purpose of system
Connection to local authority fire brigade
Zones
Explosive or flammable atmospheres
Circuit testing
Automatic indication of cable fault
Zone testing
Removal of trigger device
Standby power supplies
Remote centre

Products/Materials specific to this section

Standards
Manual call points
Detectors
Beam type detectors
Radiation (flame) detectors
Sounders
Fire alarm control panel

Workmanship specific to this section

Ancillary services
Smoke detector indicators
Manual call points
Record drawings and operating instructions

W51
Earthing and bonding

Refer to reference specification checklists

Y80   Earthing and bonding components
Y81   Testing and commissioning of electrical services
Y82   Identification - electrical
Y90   Fixing to building fabric

Generally for this section

Electrical installation metalwork
PME installations
TN-C-S (PME) systems
Existing installations

Products/Materials specific to this section

Protective conductors
Insulated gland adaptors
MICS cable terminations
Earthing clamps
Earth electrode clamps
Tape fixing devices
Earth electrodes
Earth electrode couplings
Earth electrode tape
Inspection pits
Earth electrodes in drawpits
Main earth conductor connection
Main earth conductor cover tiles
Permanent test electrodes
Earth busbars
Substation main earth busbar terminations
Frame earth tapes
Neutral/Earth connection
Test links
Equipotential bonding

Workmanship specific to this section

Installation of earthing system
Ceiling supports
Building incoming metallic services
Building services
Clean earth distribution
Tape joints
Protective cable terminations
Tape holes
Earth electrodes
Building earth bar
Building earth bar connections
Substation earth bar
Clean earth bar
Transformer earth electrode systems
Metallic fencing
Identification
Protective conductors - warning notices/labels
Main earth conductor - warning tapes
Earth bar label
Generators

W52
Lightning protection

Refer to reference specification checklists

Y80   Earthing and bonding components
Y81   Testing and commissioning of electrical services
Y82   Identification - electrical
Y90   Fixing to building fabric

Products/Materials specific to this section

Standards
Air termination
Down conductors
Earthing components
Inspection pits

Workmanship specific to this section

Bonding
Dissimilar metals

W61
Central control

Refer to reference specification checklists

Y51   Testing and commissioning of mechanical services
Y53   Control components - mechanical
Y54   Identification - mechanical
Y60   Conduit and trunking
Y61   HV/LV cables and wiring
Y63   Support components - cable
Y72   Contactors and starters
Y74   Accessories for electrical services
Y80   Earthing and bonding components
Y81   Testing and commissioning of electrical services
Y82   Identification - electrical
Y90   Fixing to building fabric
Y91   Off site painting/Anti-corrosion treatments

Generally for this section

Control system
Controls specialist
Control mode
Main power supply
Power wiring distribution
Compressed air

Y Services reference specification

Y10
Pipelines

General

Pre-fabricated pipework fittings
Fabricated fittings
Pipe joints

Products/Materials

Pipes and fittings of:
 Steel
 Cast iron
 Stainless steel
 Copper
 Lead
 Aluminium
 Unplasticised PVC
 Polyethylene
 Polypropylene
 ABS
 Vulcathene
 Nylon
 Glass
 Glass fibre reinforced

Workmanship

Appearance
Spacing
Gradients
Air vent requirements
Drain requirements
Expansion and contraction
Pipe fittings
Fabricated junctions
Fabricated fittings - ferrous
Fabricated fittings - non-ferrous
Pipes through walls and floors
Pipe sleeves
Wall, floor and ceiling masking plates
Connections to equipment
Distribution headers
Temporary plugs, caps and flanges
Welding generally
Joints:
 Material
 Type
Dissimilar metals
Pipe rings and clips
Anchors
Slide guides
Pipe supports
Support spacing
Isolation and regulation
Maintenance and renewal
Protection of underground pipework
Protection of buried pipes

Protection of pipes in screeds
Corrosion protective tape
Mechanical protective tape
Cleaning
Steel pipework
Steelwork
Non-ferrous components

Y11
Pipeline ancillaries

General

Location
Safety and relief valves - self operated - application
Steam traps and accessories
Exposed valves
Body ends
Valve operation
Testing

Products/Materials

Stop taps/valves
Regulating valves
Double regulating valves
Fixed orifice valves
Orifice plates
Regulating stations
Radiator valves
Float operated valves
Check valves
Anti back syphonage valves - combined check and anti-vacuum
Direct acting safety valves
Drain cocks
Vent cocks
Automatic air vents
Steam traps
Steam trap failure indicators
Sight glasses
Expansion loops
Expansion bellows
Compensators
Test plugs - self sealing type
Pipeline strainers
Tundishes
Temperature gauges
Pressure and altitude gauges
Vacuum gauges
Differential pressure gauges
Gauge mounting boards

Accessories

Ancillary fittings
Loose items

Workmanship

Installation
Positioning of components
Positioning of double regulating variable orifice valve
Positioning of regulating station
Vent cocks
Valve stuffing boxes
Discharge connections
Expansion devices
Expansion bellows installation
Compensator installation
Hose compensators installation

Y20
Pumps

General

Pumps
Pump selection

Products/Materials

Casing
Impeller
Shafts
Bearings
Glands and seals
Drive
Suction and delivery connections
Pumps

Accessories

Safety guards
Drive belts
Matching flanges

Workmanship

Pipeline connections
Drain lines from packed and water-cooled glands
Mountings
Alignment
Access
Maintenance requirements for sewage pumps

Y21
Water tanks/cisterns

General

Tank design
Definitions

Products/Materials

Tanks:
    Material
    Type
Cisterns:
    Material
    Type

Accessories

Contents gauges
Level alarms
Level switches
Electric heaters
Ball valve boxes
Accessories connections
Ventilation cowls
Standing overflows
Warning pipes

Workmanship

Protection and cleaning
Inspection and access

Y22
Heat exchangers

General
Heat exchanger design

Products/Materials
Heat exchangers

Workmanship
Flange drillings
Protection and cleaning
Inspection
Rust protection

Y23
Storage cylinders/calorifiers

General
Standards
Definitions

Products/Materials
Cylinders:
  Material
  Type
Hot water storage combination units
Calorifiers

Workmanship
Flange drillings
Protection and cleaning
Inspection and cleaning

Y24
Trace Heating

General
Standards

Products/Materials
Trace heating
Heating blankets

Workmanship
Installation of electric trace heating
Installation of piped trace heating
Installation of heating blankets
Insulation

Y25
Cleaning and chemical treatment

General
Conditions for cleaning and chemical treatment
Cleaning and chemical treatment specialist
Mains water analysis
Preliminary checks
Procedural precautions

Products/Materials
Dosing - closed systems
Dosing - cooling towers
Chemicals
Softening
Metering and sampling

Workmanship
Flushing
Purging
Chemical cleaning and solids removal
Sterilization - general
Sterilization - mains water system
Sterilization - water storage systems
Water treatment for boilers
Service visits
Documentation

101

Y30
Air ductlines

General

Ductwork design
Ductwork dimensions
Design information
Electrical bonding terminal

Products/Materials

Ductwork:
  Material
  Type
Plant connections
Flanged connections
Safety of cut edges

Accessories

Flexible joints
Sealants, gaskets and tapes
Protective finishes
Splitters
Turning vanes - low and medium pressure
Turning vanes - high pressure

Workmanship

Access
Drainage of ductwork
Connection to builder's work
Spacing of supports
Ductwork vibration isolation
Flexible ductwork
Expansion joints - plastic ducts
Protection and cleaning
Weatherproofing
Ductwork sleeves
Fire rated ductwork sleeves
Test holes
Holes for control equipment
Installation of control equipment
Ductwork air leakage testing

Y31
Air ductline ancillaries

Products/Materials

Access openings
Access and inspection covers
Access doors
Hangers and supports
Proprietary supports
Control dampers
Motorized control dampers
Fire dampers
Fire damper accessories
Fire damper fusible links
Smoke dampers
Pressure control flaps
Pressure relief dampers
Shut off damper
Non return damper
Bird wire guards
Insect guards

Workmanship

Construction and finishes
Access cover restraint
Access door handles
Access opening safety
Access door insulation
Ductwork supports
Vapour barriers
Accessory support
External ductwork support
Ductwork floor supports
Appearance of ductwork supports
Fire precautions
Fire damper access
Positioning
Instrument connections
Testing

Y40
Air handling units

General
Location
Design duties
Air leakage

Products/Materials
Air handling units
Air handling unit access

Accessories
Fan section
Filter section
Heater batteries
Cooling coil section
Humidifier section
Sound attenuators
Vibration isolation
Control dampers
Face and bypass dampers
Mixing section
Intake louvres

Workmanship
Component assembly
Access
Humidifier installation
Duct connections
Services connections
Isolation of units
Drainage of free water
Support air handling unit
Testing

Y41
Fans

General
Fan location
Approved firms
Design duties
Operating conditions
Construction and handling
Protection
Testing
Variable air volume fans

Products/Materials
Motor
Drive
Fans

Accessories
Inspection doors
Guards
Connections to duct
Guide vanes - axial fans
Guide vanes - centrifugal fans
Guide vanes - mixed flow fans
Shutters
Air flow sensors
Access
Mounting
Speed controller
Standby motor

Workmanship
Location
Attitude
Alignment
Testing
Drain connection

Y42
Air filtration

General
Duty and performance
Capacity and efficiency
Location
Seals
Casings
Filter testing
Access

Products/Materials
Filters
Electrostatic precipators

Accessories
Instruments
Filter housing
Terminal filter housing
Safe change filter changing unit
Spares
Cleaning
Mounting frames

Workmanship
Assembly
Access for maintenance

Y43
Heating/Cooling coils

General
Location
Design duties

Products/Materials
Coils
Air washer

Accessories
Drip trays
Eliminator plates
Mounting frame
Matching flanges - ductwork
Matching flanges - pipework
Anti-freeze thermostat
Auto air purging valve
Access doors
Access walkway
Viewing window
Lighting
Air flow switch
Water treatment

Workmanship
Position/location
Connections
Coil support
Protection

Y44
Humidifiers

General
Humidifiers
Design duties
General design
Protection

Products/Materials
Humidifiers

Accessories
Access doors
Inspection windows
Walkways
Lighting
Spreader plate
Eliminator section
Water treatment
Duct connections

Workmanship
Position/location
Assembly
Condensate connections
Thermal expansion
Drain traps
Fixings

Y45
Silencers/Acoustic treatment

General
Design duties
Fire properties
Testing

Products/Materials
Silencers:
   Material
   Shape
Acoustic splitters
Air transfer/cross talk attenuators
Acoustic linings
Plenums
Acoustic flexible duct connectors
Acoustic louvres
Acoustic doors
Acoustic enclosures
Acoustic floating floor panels
Acoustic wall lining panels
Cable access floor panels

Workmanship
Acoustic enclosures
Access to acoustic enclosures
Supports
Acoustic linings
Sound power level readings

Y46
Grilles/Diffusers/Louvres

General

Performance
Size
Noise levels
Electrical bonding terminal
Protective wrapping
Grille construction
Diffuser construction
Louvre construction
Grille mounting
Diffuser mounting
Louvre fixings

Products/Materials

Grilles
Diffusers
Laminar flow panels
Louvres - external air supply/extract type
Louvres/Screen walling

Accessories

Dampers
Air flow deflectors
Blanking plates
Perforated baffle plates
Perforated screens
Ceiling or wall mounted plenum boxes
Floor mounted plenum boxes
Louvre access panels and doors
Spares

Workmanship

Grille/diffuser location
Louvre location
Accessories
Connection to ductwork
Installation in builders work
Transfer grilles
Fixing

Y50
Thermal insulation

General

Temperature range
Standards
Materials
Spread of flame
Pre-insulated equipment
Electrical bonding terminal

Products/Materials

Thermal conductivity
Insulation:
    Material
    Type
Facings integral with sectional material
Facings applied in situ
Vapour barrier coatings
Vapour barrier reinforcement
Flame retardant coatings
Adhesives
Protection materials
Reinforcement
Preformed rigid sections and slabs
Valve and flange boxes
Heat exchangers and other vessels
Water tanks
Boiler flues
Pre-insulated boiler flues
Pre-insulated storage vessels
Cylinder jackets
Pumps and other irregular shapes

Workmanship

Separation
Clearance
Application
Finish
Flanges and valves
Liners
Preformed rigid sections
Pipeline supports
Pipe sleeves
Ductwork supports
Duct sleeves
Valve and flange boxes
Vapour barriers - liquid
Vapour barriers - sheet
Integrity of vapour barriers
Protection
Application of weather proof paints
Inspection and testing
Thickness of insulation

Y51
Testing and commissioning of mechanical services

Static testing

Pressure testing:
  General
  Water circulating and supply systems steam and condense lines
  Underground pipework
  Water mains
  Fire risers
  Gas pipework
  Piped medical services
  Soil, waste, ventilation, anti-syphon and rainwater pipework
  Underslab drainage
Vacuum testing
Testing records

Commissioning

Cleaning ductwork systems
Commissioning codes
Preliminary checks - water distribution
Preliminary checks - air distribution
Setting to work and regulation - water distribution
Setting to work and regulation - air distribution
Commissioning boiler plant
Commissioning refrigerating systems
Commissioning automatic control systems
Commissioning plant items
Instruments and gauges
Commissioning records

Performance testing

System performance testing
Environmental tests
Recorders
Testing to specified conditions
Performance test records

Y52
Vibration isolation mountings

General

Design intent
Spring anti vibration mountings
Spring hangers
Locking facility

Products/Materials

Mountings
Hangers
Inertia bases
Vibration isolation hoses
Pipework vibration isolation
Pipe wall and riser seals

Workmanship

Cast in situ bases
Fixing
Horizontally restrained spring mountings

Y53
Control components - mechanical

General

Control components
Control wiring
Panels/Enclosures
Ancillaries
Local instruments
Discrimination
Drawings

Products/Materials

Thermostatic radiator valves
Thermostatic control valves
Pressure reducing valves
Pressure control valves - direct acting type
Motorized valves
Motorized dampers
Motorized shutters
Actuators
Detectors and sensors - general
Detectors:
  Temperature
  Humidity
  Pressure
  Flow
  Level
  Other
Air thermostats
Immersion thermostats
Humidistats
Recorders
Controllers
Lights and alarms
Audible alarms
Transmitters
Amplifiers
Optimisers
Programmers
Compensators
Time switches
Transducers
Control circuits
Control circuit transformers
Current transformers
Enclosures

Workmanship

General
Appearance
Insulation
Supports
Access
Pressure reducing and control valves
Self operating controls
Power operated controls
Electric motor actuators
Sensors/controllers
Ancillaries
Enclosures

Y54
Identification - mechanical

General

Requirements
New systems
Existing systems
Colours

Products/Materials

Pipework identification
Ductwork identification
Plant and equipment identification
Valve and cock identification
Medical gas terminal units
Laboratory outlets
Air volume regulating and control damper identification
Instrument identification
Danger and warning notices
System identification installation charts

Y60
Conduit and cable trunking

General

Standards

Products/Materials

Conduit:
   Material
   Type
   Fittings
Trunking:
   Material
   Type
   Fittings
Service outlet boxes
Surface trunking of insulating materials
Underfloor trunking of insulating materials
Supports and fixings

Workmanship

Layout
Spacing
Condensation prevention
Screwed steel conduit
Steel conduit fittings
Draw-in boxes
Installation of conduit in screed
Conduit boxes
Underground installation
Wiring
Fixing conduit
Flexible and pliable conduit
Non-meticallic conduit
Steel trunking
Fixing trunking
Fire barriers
Underfloor trunking installation
Trunking of insulating material
Access
Protection and repair of steel components
Cleaning before wiring
Equipment connection

Y61
HV/LV cables and wiring

General

Cable manufacturer
Cable certification marking
HV cable records

Products/Materials

Insulated flexible cords:
  Material
  Type
Insulated cables:
  Material
  Type

Accessories

Cable glands
Cable solder-type sockets
Cable compression joints and connectors
Cable fitting compound
Insulating tapes - pressure sensitive
Varnished fabric insulating tapes
Soft solders for cable terminations
Cable ducts

Workmanship

Cable installation - general
Cable trenches
Cable installation in trenches
Cable ducts
Cable installation in ducts
Cable installation in conduit and trunking
Cable installation on tray and rack
Cable surface installation
Cable installation - mineral insulated cables
Cable installation - flexible cords
Cable jointing and terminating generally
Cable jointing and terminating - paper insulated cables
Cable jointing and terminating - elastomer and plastic insulated cables
Cable jointing and terminating - mineral insulated cables
Cable sleeves

Y62
Busbar trunking

General

Busbar systems

Products/Materials

Enclosure construction
Busbars
Busbar finish
Tap-off units
Protective conductors

Workmanship

Termination
Fixings
Connections
Expansion
Marking
Fire barriers

Y63
Support components - cables

General

Cable supports
Cable support system finishes

Products/Materials

Cable tray
Cable tray fittings
Cable rack
Cable rack fittings
Cable special support systems
Cable hangers
Cable cleats
Cable ties
Cable clips and saddles

Workmanship

Cable tray installation
Cable cleats, ties, saddles and clips installation

Y71
LV switchgear and distribution boards

General

Standard
Type test
Site built assemblies
Site modification
Electrical characteristics

Products/Materials

Enclosures
Enclosures finish
Terminals for external conductors
Terminal blocks for auxiliary wiring
Switchboards
Battery charger sets
Circuit breakers
Air break switches
Voltage sensing relays
Trip/Close switches and control selector switches
Current transformers
Instruments and meters
Indicator lights
Padlocks
Low voltage coils rating
Framework
Fuses
Miniature circuit-breakers
Residual current-operated circuit breakers
Distribution boards
Consumer units
Cable terminations

Workmanship

Fixing
Mounting height
Access
Marking
Cable terminations

Y72
Contactors and starters

Products/Materials

LV contactors
Coil power supply
Paired contactor mechanical and electrical interlocks
Auxiliary circuit contact
Co-ordination with short circuit protection devices
Enclosures
In-built isolating switches
In-built control selector switches
In-built push buttons
In-built indicator lights
Contactor control relays
Control and indicator light circuit fuses
Motor starters
Automatic changeover for run/standby duty:
   Single power supply
   Dual power supply
Motors - overcurrent protection

Workmanship

Installation

Y73
Luminaires and lamps

General

Standards

Products/Materials

Luminaires
Lampholders
Control gear and components
Lamps
Support system
Columns and bollards

Accessories

Track lighting
Integral photo-cells
Air handling luminaires

Workmanship

Installation
Support
Suspension
Columns and bollards
Connections to luminaires

Y74
Accessories for electrical services

General
Application
Samples

Products/Materials
Interior lighting switches
Exterior lighting switches
Time switches
Luminaire connectors
Lampholders
Isolating switches
Switched fuse connection units
Switched socket-outlets
Cord outlets
Cable and appliance couplers
Telephone outlet sockets
Telephone cord outlets
Multipin connectors
VDU BNC sockets
Aerial sockets
Low voltage isolating transformer units
Shaver points
Indicator lamps

Workmanship
Earthing
Protection
Fixing

Y80
Earthing and bonding components

General
Electrical installation metalwork

Products/Materials
Lugs/Tags
Protective cable terminations
Protective conductor warning notices/labels
External sockets and equipment

Workmanship
Clean earth distribution

Y81
Testing and commissioning of electrical services

General
Inspection and test procedures
Standby generators
HV and LV switchgear
HV power transformers
Site inspection and testing
Specialist installations
Records
Completion certificates
Inspection certificates for alterations to existing installations
Record documentation
Supply characteristics
Incorporated equipment characterics
Physical inspection
Setting and adjustments

Products/Materials
Test equipment and consumables
Calibration

Workmanship
Site installation tests
Continuity of protective conductors
Conductive parts
Phase sequence
Earth fault loop impedance (ZS)
Prospective short circuit current (IP)
High voltage tests
Cables
Conduit, trunking and ducting

Y82
Identification - electrical

General
Application
Material
Fixing
Arrangement
Conductor arrangement

Products/Materials
Danger labels
Plant and equipment lables
Motors and starters lables
Engraved switchplates
Switchgear
Distribution boards
Earthing
Indicator lamps for power systems - meaning of colour signals
Conduit and trunking colour coding
Cable identification
Underground cable identification
Cabling colour coding

Y90
Fixing to building fabric

General
Preparation
Manufacturer's drawings
Cast-in fixings
Building-in by others
Size of fixings
Greasing of fixings

Products/Materials
Standards
Plugs
Screws
Shot fired fixings
Self adhesive fixings
Proprietary channel inserts

Workmanship
Drilling
Proprietary fixings
Fixing to reinforced concrete
Fixing to brickwork
Fixing to timber rails
Fixing to hollow stud/tile/block walls
Fixing to concrete, brickwork or blockwork
Fixing to metalwork
Fixing to structural steelwork and concrete structures

Y91
Off-site painting/Anti-corrosion treatments

General
General requirements
Damaged finishes

Products/Materials
Paint materials
Paint quality
Heat resistant paint

Workmanship
Weather and other conditions
Cleaning
Application off-site
Application
Cold galvanizing
Protection of bright machine parts
Special protective finishes

Y92
Motor drives - electric

General
Standards
Electrical supply
Electrical equipment
Performance characteristics
Operating conditions
Interference suppression
Mounting
Keys

Products/Materials
Motors - general
Motor ratings
Motors - overcurrent protection
Motor starters
Automatic changeover for run/standby duty:
   Single power supply
   Dual power supply
Indirect drives
Direct coupled drives
Guards

Z Building fabric reference specification

Z10
Purpose made joinery

Suitability of timber and rigid sheets for purpose, where species, type, class, grade, etc are not specified

General quality of timber

Moisture content at time of manufacture and fixing:
  External
  Internal, intermittent heating
  Internal, continuous heating

Testing moisture content

Maintaining moisture content

Preservative/flame retardant treatment of timber:
  Moisture content at time of treatment
  Licensing of processor
  Certificates of compliance with specification
  Limits on processing after treatment
  Treatment of surfaces exposed by minor cutting

Protection and storage of timber and components

Machinery and jointing

Suitability and quality of adhesives

Applying veneers and laminates

Jointing trims

Sealing end grains

Surface sanding

Priming/Sealing before leaving shop (reference to section Z30)

Mechanical fastenings:
  Nailing
  Screwing
  Pelleting

Z11
Purpose made metalwork

Suitability of materials for purpose, where type, grade, etc. are not specified

Compliance of materials with Standards:
  Mild steel
  Cold rolled steel
  Stainless steel
  Aluminium alloy
  Copper alloy

Jointing and fabrication generally

Welding:
  Steel
  Stainless steel
  Aluminium alloys

Brazing, bronze welding

Grinding and cleaning of visible welded joints

Mechanical fastenings:
  Generally
  Machine screws
  Self-tapping screws
  Bolts
  Rivets

Bedding compound to mechanical joints

Adhesive bonding

Compliance of coatings with Standards:
  Galvanizing
  Zinc plating
  Cadmium plating
  Chromium plating
  Sherardizing
  Vitreous enamelling
  Anodizing

Finishes:
  Ground
  Brush
  Buffed
  Polished

Z20
Fixings/Adhesives

Fixings

General suitability for purpose

Compatibility with product/material being fixed and fixed to

Corrosion resistance:
   Where directly exposed to the weather, water or corrosive atmospheres
   Where used in construction elements exposed to the weather, etc.

Sizes, lengths, spacings

Plugs

Fixing through finishes

Adhesives

General suitability for purpose

Compatibility with product/material being fixed and fixed to

Weather/water/moisture resistance

Observance of manufacturers recommendations:
   Shelf life
   Mixing
   Open time
   Application and use

Safety precautions

Z21
Mortars

Sand generally

Lime:sand mixes:
   Ready-mixed
   Coloured ready mixed
   Site mixed

Cement generally

Admixtures generally

Water

Use of retarded ready-mixed mortars

Batching

Mixing

Cleanliness of plant and banker boards

Restrictions on timing of use of mortar

Z22
Sealants

Compatibility with products/materials being jointed

Checking dimensions of joints against manufacturer's recommendations for usage

Depth of sealant

Cleaning and preparing joint faces

Masking adjacent surfaces

Applying primers, inserting backing strips

Applying preformed or gun grade sealants and pointing

Z30
Off-site painting

Checking compatibility of materials

Moisture content of backgrounds

Weather and other conditions

Preparation materials

Preparation of surfaces:
   Timber for painting
   Timber for clear coating
   Manual cleaning of steel
   Blast cleaning of steel
   Aluminium
   UPVC

Application of coatings generally

Special methods of application

Part C
Libraries of clauses

Section 7.3 recommends the use of an appropriate library of specification clauses and lists the features which such libraries should exhibit. A model procedure for preparing specifications is given in Section 7.4 and assumes use of a library of clauses.

This part of the Code illustrates the following commercially available libraries of specification clauses:

National Building Specification

Sponsored by the RIBA, and available from NBS Services Ltd on subscription in two versions – 'Full' and 'Intermediate' (abridged). Both versions are available on disk for use with a wide range of computers and word processors. Coverage includes virtually all architectural and structural types of work, together with simple mechanical and electrical installations. It is planned to re-issue NBS in CAWS format to all current subscribers during 1988.

National Engineering Specification

Sponsored by CIBSE, and available from NES Ltd on subscription in three volumes and on floppy disks for use with word processing packages and specification generating programs. Coverage includes the types of work most commonly specified by services engineers, and it is planned that the scope will be expanded progressively. NES is structured in accordance with CAWS.

National Building Specification

NBS is illustrated by selected pages from the 'Intermediate' Version of Section E10 In situ concrete. In order that these can be seen in context, the contents of all pages included in the section are summarised below:

E10 In situ concrete

Scope of section

General guidance notes   * Page 1

Specification of mixes by reference to BS 5328.

Basic types of mix: designed and prescribed.

| Table of ordinary prescribed mixes | Page 2 |

| Durability of concrete | * Page 3 |

| Durability of concrete (continued) | Page 4 |

Table showing resistance to sulphate attack

| Table showing suitability for general purposes | Page 5 |

| Table showing durability of structural concrete | Page 6 |

Specification clauses with side notes

| Types of mix – designed | * Page 7 |

| Types of mix – designed/prescribed | Page 8 |

| Types of mix – prescribed | Page 9 |

General clauses

| Constituent materials | * Page 10 |

| Design/Batching and mixing | * Page 11 |

Testing/Certification of concrete

| Placing and compacting | Page 12 |

| Curing and protecting | Page 13 |

| Curing and protecting (continued) | Page 14 |

* Pages 1, 3, 7, 10 and 11 are illustrated and are highlighted accordingly. On pages 7, 10 and 11, clauses have been marked up to illustrate use on a project.

SCOPE

This section covers the manufacture, testing and use of structural quality in situ concrete and should be used in conjunction with the separate NBS sections for formwork, reinforcement, worked finishes and joints. The Intermediate Version does not cover the following, and reference should be made to the Full Version:

BS 5328 special prescribed mixes
Testing of constituent materials
Watertight concrete
Clauses for workmanship in constructing walls and columns
Testing of concrete structures

GENERAL GUIDANCE NOTES

1 SPECIFICATION OF CONCRETE MIXES

1.1 General

BS 8110:1985 'Structural use of concrete' largely avoids covering the same ground as BS 5328 'Methods for specifying concrete'. Specification of concrete mixes can thus be based entirely on BS 5328, choice of mixes being guided by the recommendations of BS 8110.

BS 5328 gives the following definitions:

'Prescribed mix: a mix for which the purchaser specifies the proportions of the constituents and is responsible for ensuring that the proportions prescribed will produce a concrete with the performance he requires'.

'Designed mix: a mix for which the purchaser is responsible for specifying the required performance and the producer is responsible for selecting the mix proportions to produce the required performance'.

1.2 Designed mixes

Designed mixes offer the Architect and Engineer a direct assurance that the concrete complies with the strength requirement. They involve the making, curing and testing of cubes and the checking of test results. Hitherto, the compliance rules have proved to be somewhat difficult to operate unless concrete is used in moderately large quantities during the early stages and on a fairly regular basis thereafter. These difficulties have now been significantly reduced because:

The compliance rules of BS 5328 lay down a fixed margin so that it is no longer necessary to establish the current margin for each job.

Most in situ concrete is now supplied ready mixed and 90% of all ready mixed concrete depots in the UK are accredited under the Quality Scheme for Ready Mixed Concrete (QSRMC). Where concrete is obtained from such a depot and use is irregular the designer can use the producer's data as alternative evidence of compliance (see clause 650).

In this way the expense of trial mixes can usually be avoided, and the cost of routine testing is considerably reduced. It is therefore now practicable to specify designed mixes for medium size and even small projects.

1.3 Ordinary prescribed mixes

Table 1 of BS 5328 defines the proportions of cement and aggregates in a range of 'Ordinary prescribed mixes' which can be expected to have at least the strength indicated by the grade number. A typical designation is C20P, in which 'C' means compressive strength, the number indicates the 28 day characteristic strength in N/mm², and 'P' means ordinary prescribed mix. Strength testing is not used to judge compliance, the producer's responsibility being only to produce concrete of the specified proportions. Ordinary prescribed mixes may contain only certain of the more common types of cement and aggregates. Admixtures are prohibited.

The specification of ordinary prescribed mixes is very simple, and cube testing is not required. Their use may therefore be appropriate on small jobs.

Variations in the properties of cement and aggregate from different sources mean that the actual strengths of ordinary prescribed mixes vary considerably. In order to ensure that the indicative strength is attained in all cases, ordinary prescribed mixes normally have a high cement content and characteristic strength when compared with designed mixes of the same nominal grade. For example a C25P ordinary prescribed mix will usually have a cement content and strength similar to a C40 designed mix. Because the cement content is higher, the cost of prescribed mixes is higher than designed of the same grade.

C&CA publication 45.031 'Concrete for general purposes' defines a range of ordinary prescribed mixes which, for all practical purposes, the same as the BS 5328 mixes (see table A). All these mixes are made with an assumed nominal maximum size of and the workability is assumed out the proportion practicable way use on small jo site. NBS c ordinary pr C&CA pub

1.4 Speci

Page 1

The scope of the section is the same as section E10 of CAWS, but is not listed in detail here. The note is mainly concerned to describe exclusions from the NBS Intermediate Version.

General guidance notes, which start here, occupy six of the fourteen pages in the section. When the side notes to clauses are taken into account, 70% of the section comprises guidance notes, only 30% clauses. The emphasis is thus on helping the specifier take the right decisions, reducing the need for him to read other documents.

2 DURABILITY OF CONCRETE

2.1 Background

The durability of concrete has been a matter of concern for many years and there is now a widely held belief that we have a large legacy of buildings with concrete affected by exposure to the elements, with corroding reinforcement and consequential spalling. Despite this, durable concrete is attainable with a good deal of certainty.

2.2 Factors affecting durability

Concrete which is not adequately designed to meet the anticipated exposure conditions may fail to be durable in two ways. First, the concrete itself may suffer from frost or chemical action causing either surface spalling or, in severe cases, complete disruption. Second, the reinforcing steel may suffer from corrosion, the by-products of which cause expansion and spalling/cracking of the concrete cover.

The ability of the concrete to resist these tendencies depends on:

The degree of exposure to weather and aggressive chemicals.
The depth of concrete cover to the reinforcement.
The permeability of the concrete.
Limiting the presence of reactive ingredients in the aggregates, cement and any admixtures.
In certain circumstances, the use of chemically resistant cements.

Low permeability is necessary so that the surface zone of concrete can resist the entry of harmful liquids, vapours and gases. Carbon dioxide in the atmosphere penetrates the concrete and over a period of time results in carbonation, or loss of alkalinity – an alkaline environment is necessary to prevent rusting of reinforcement. Water and oxygen are necessary for the corrosion of steel. Chlorides from de-icing salts, sea water or sea spray, or from any of the constituent materials will accelerate that corrosion. Sulphates from the ground or ground water may disrupt the concrete.

The factors which determine the ability of the concrete to resist these aggressive agents are discussed in the following paragraphs. Their relevance in relation to various uses and exposure conditions for concrete is shown in the following Tables:
Table B, page 5 Sulphate attack
Table C, page 5 Concrete for general purposes
Table D, page 6 Structural concrete.

2.3 Type of cement

In most circumstances the type of cement used is secondary to the amount of cement, free water/cement ratio, compaction and curing. However in certain circumstances durability requirements will justify the specification of particular types of cement.

In this regard, it is worth calling attention to the increasing availability and use of pulverized fuel ash (PFA) and ground-granulated blastfurnace slag (GGBS) as cementitious materials. They may be available pre-blended with cement but it is more common for them to be combined in the mixer with ordinary Portland cement.

Where sulphates are present in the ground or ground water, sulphate resisting Portland cement or combinations of GGBS/OPC or PFA/OPC may be necessary – see table B on page 5.

Where concrete is exposed to de-icing salts, sea water or a marine environment, the risk of reinforcement corrosion will be high. Although not recognised in BS 8110, there is evidence (available from manufacturers) that combinations of GGBS with OPC give higher resistance to the diffusion of chlorides than OPC alone. However if GGBS/OPC concrete is used the depths of cover required by BS 8110, table 3.4 must not be reduced and longer curing times will be necessary. Sulphate resisting Portland cement has a relatively poor resistance to chlorides – see BS 8110: Part 1, clause 3.3.5.6.

Alkali-silica reaction in concrete has been widely publicised, but in practice it is a rare occurrence. Where the aggregates are suspect, combinations of GGBS or PFA with OPC can be used to reduce the level of reactive alkali in the cement to a safe level.

2.4 Amount of cement

In recent years there have been major advances in cement and concrete technology. Two developments stand out:
The performance of cement has increased markedly, for example the strength of standard mixes using ordinary Portland cement increased by 25% between 1960 and 1982.
The use of ready mixed concrete has grown from a negligible amount in 1950 to more than two thirds of in situ concrete now. Ready mix plants manufacture more consistent concrete than can be made on all but the largest and best organised construction sites. The mix design should be under the control of a skilled and experienced technologist so that any required target strength is consistently achieved.

The result has been that cement contents for given strengths of concrete have fallen, with adverse effects on the permeability of concrete, and hence its durability.

Cement contents for durability are laid down in BS 8110, tables 3.4, 6.1 and 6.2, and are summarised in table D on page 6.

2.5 Free water/cement ratio

As cement contents have fallen in relation to strengths of concrete, free water/cement ratios have risen, as shown by the following table:

Typical strengths (N/mm²)

| 1960 | 52 | 45 | 35 | 27 | 21 |
| 1980 | 72 | 56 | 44 | 35 | 27 |

| Typical W/C ratios | 0.4 | 0.5 | 0.6 | 0 | |

The combined effect of high W/C ratios ha~ permeable concrete, ~ ment. Free water/~ now laid down ~ stringent tha~ CP 110 and ~ page 6.

Page 3

Because of industry concern about the durability of concrete, four pages of general guidance notes are given summarising the most recent recommendations of the British Standards Institution, the Cement and Concrete Association and the ready mixed concrete industry. The key reference document is BS 8110: Part 1: 1985 'Structural use of concrete', and it is assumed that the specifier will have a copy.

E10   IN SITU CONCRETE

To be read in conjunction with Preliminaries/General conditions.

TYPES OF MIX

Delete sub-items which do not apply. Repeat the mix type items as required.

Complete clause numbers, e.g. 101, 102, etc.

DESIGNED MIXES

Complete mix type item(s) as follows:

CONCRETE FOR _ _ _ _ _ _ _ _ _ _ _ _:

Insert, e.g.
'SUSPENDED SLABS AND COLUMNS'
'STRIP FOOTINGS'.

Grade:

Insert one of the following: C2.5, C5, C7.5, C10, C12.5, C15, C20, C25, C30, C35, C40, C45, C50, C55, C60.

In many cases structural strength will not be the only consideration. The durability of the concrete will often be critical – see general guidance notes 1.2, 2.6 and table D on page 6.

Cement(s):

In most cases it will be appropriate to insert *'as BS 5328'*. Particular type(s) of cement can be specified if required, the readily available types being:

Ordinary Portland cement (OPC)
Rapid hardening Portland cement (RHPC)
White Portland cement (WCP)
Portland blastfurnace cement (PBC)
Portland pulverized-fuel ash cement (PPFAC)
Sulphate resisting Portland cement (SRPC)
Ground-granulated blastfurnace slag (GGBS) or pulverized-fuel ash (PFA) combined in the mixer with OPC.

If a GGBS or PFA/OPC combination is required it will be necessary to state the proportions, e.g *'70-90% GGBS with OPC'*.

Aggregate(s):

In most cases it will be appropriate to insert *'as BS 5328'*. Particular type(s) can be specified if required.

Nominal maximum size of aggregate:

Standard sizes are 40, 20, 14 and 10 mm. 20 mm is normal. 40 mm is often more economic but is too large for most reinforced work. 14 mm is not normally available.

Minimum cement content:

This may be necessary to give adequate durability – see general guidance note 2.4 and tables B and D. If an 'equivalent strength grade for durability' is specified, it is nevertheless advisable to also specify the minimum cement content.

(continued overleaf)

TYPES OF MIX

 CONCRETE FOR FOUNDATIONS, MANHOLES AND EXTERNAL STAIR
- Designed mix to BS 5328, Grade C50
- Cement(s): 25-40% PFA + OPC, or 70-90% GGBFS + OPC
- Aggregate(s):   Coarse: BS 882
                         Fine: BS 882
- Nominal maximum size of aggregate: 20 mm
- Minimum cement content: 380 kg/m³
- Maximum free-water/cement ratio: 0.45
- ~~Maximum cement content:~~ _ _ _ kg/m³
- ~~Admixture:~~ _
- Rate of sampling for compressive strength testing: one sample per 50 m³ but not less than one for each day of use.

102 CONCRETE FOR GROUND SLAB, SUSPENDED SLAB, INTERNAL STAIR:
- Designed mix to BS 5328, Grade C30
- Cement(s): as BS 5328
- Aggregate(s):   Coarse: BS 882
                         Fine: BS 882
- Nominal maximum size of aggregate: 20 mm
- Minimum cement content: 275 kg/m³
- Maximum free-water/cement ratio: 0.65
- ~~Maximum cement content:~~ _ _ _ kg/m³
- ~~Admixture:~~ _
- Rate of sampling for compressive strength testing: one sample per 50 m³ but not less than one for each day of use.

Page 7

The specification clauses, with side notes, start here. The first sub-section is for 'Types of mix', containing 'work type clauses' as described in section 6.2 of this Code.

The clauses have been completed to specify the concrete mixes for a medium sized project. Designed mixes are specified rather than prescribed, in order to give better quality assurance.

The choice of mixes has been rationalised in that type E10/101 is to be used for both concrete in the foundations and manholes (exposed to a high concentration of sulphates in the ground water) and concrete in an external stair (exposed to de-icing salts and frost action).

Mix E10/102 is for less severely exposed structural concrete.

210
Always include this clause. Reference to BS 5328 permits the considerable abbreviation of project specifications.

230, 231
Alternative clauses.
See the QSRMC Regulations.

(210) COMPLIANCE WITH BS 5328: constituent materials, composition of mixes, production of concrete, information to be provided, sampling, testing and compliance to be in accordance with BS 5328 unless otherwise specified.

~~230~~ READY MIXED CONCRETE may be used provided that it is obtained from a plant which holds a current Certificate of Accreditation under the Quality Scheme for Ready Mixed Concrete. Each mix must be obtained from only one source unless otherwise approved. Confirm name and address of depot(s) to SO before any concrete is delivered. Retain all delivery notes for inspection.

231
For use where close quality control of the concrete is required and the Contractor's facilities for this purpose may be inadequate. Very small deliveries of ready mixed concrete may be uneconomic, the normal capacity of a truck mixer being about 6 m³.

Use of ready mixed concrete will be particularly advantageous where:

. Designed mix(es) are being specified – see clause 650.
. High strength or high durability concretes are being specified.

Insert appropriate details, e.g. *'mix type E10/102'*.

(231) READY MIXED CONCRETE must be used for mix types E10/101 and E10/102 , and must be obtained from a plant which holds a current Certificate of Accreditation under the Quality Scheme for Ready Mixed Concrete. Each mix must be obtained from only one source unless otherwise approved. Confirm name and address of depot(s) to SO before any concrete is delivered. Retain all delivery notes for inspection.

CONSTITUENT MATERIALS

320
The total chloride content should be calculated from the mix proportions and the measured chloride content of each of the constituents, including any admixtures.

Admixtures containing calcium chloride should normally not be specified or approved – see clause 590.

(320) CHLORIDE CONTENT OF MIXES: the total chloride ion content of the constituents of each mix, expressed as a percentage by weight of cement (including GGBS or PFA if used) in the mix, must not exceed the following:
- Prestressed concrete: 0.1
- Concrete made with sulphate resisting
- Portland cement or supersulphated cement: 0.2
  Concrete made with Portland cement,
  Portland blastfurnace cement or
  combinations of GGBS or PFA with
  ordinary Portland cement and containing
  embedded metal: 0.4

Submit calculations demonstrating compliance.

330
See BS 5328, Appendix A.4 and C&CA Publication 45.016 'Impurities in concreting aggregates'.

(330) SULPHATE CONTENT OF MIXES: the total sulphate content of the constituents of each mix, expressed as SO3, must not exceed 4% by weight of the cement in the mix. Submit calculations demonstrating compliance.

470
Cement stored in bulk in a silo may still be satisfactory for up to about three months. However, cement in the normal 3-ply paper bags stored under good conditions can lose significant strength (about 20%) after 4 to 6 weeks.

A check should be made occasionally to ensure that the cement is not 'air-set', i.e. contains partly hardened lumps. Air-set cement results from moisture present in the air slowly seeping through paper, if in bags, and being absorbed by the cement.

~~470~~ STORAGE OF CEMENT:
- Arrange delivery in suitably small consignments so th cement will be used within 4 weeks of delivery.
- Deliver in undamaged, dry sealed bags or purpos bulk delivery vehicles.
- Store dry in weathertight structures with a r or in suitable silos.
- Store different consignments (if bagged) separately and use in order of delivery
- Reject any cement which is set such easily crumbled between the fingers

480
Sands are usually delivered with moisture contents between 7% and 10% and even up to 15%. With such variability it is difficult for the mixer operator to regulate the amount of water in the mix, leading to variations in water–cement ratio and strength. Sand which has been stockpiled for about 16 hours will, under normal weather conditions, have a moisture content of about 5%.

~~480~~ STORAGE OF AGGREGATE
- Store different aggreg
  self-drained areas o
- Check by visual i
  each batch befor
  shape, accura
  and cleanlin
- Ensure co
  at time
  drain

Page 10

These clauses, and those on the succeeding pages, are 'clauses to support the work type clauses' as described in section 6.2 of this Code.

The site is in an urban location within easy reach of several ready mixed concrete plants. There is a strong preference for quality assured concrete so clause 231 has been chosen in preference to 230. Consequent on this clauses 470 and 480, specifying the site storage of materials, could be deleted.

DESIGN/BATCHING AND MIXING

510

Available test data on the strength of concrete mixes can be supplied by QSRMC Accredited Plants and will obviate the need for trial mixes.

(510) EVIDENCE OF SUITABILITY: for each designed mix, before making concrete for use in the works and whenever a change in the materials or mix proportions is proposed, submit and obtain approval of:
- Details of proposed quantities of each ingredient per cubic metre of compacted concrete and proposed workability.
- Either existing data or details of appropriate tests on trial mixes to show that the proposed constituent materials and method of manufacture will produce concrete of the required quality, which will not segregate or bleed and will be capable of being fully compacted.

530

See general guidance note 1.3. Use this clause if it is likely that the concrete will be mixed on site.

BS 5328 permits volume batching for C7.5P, C10P and C15P mixes, but not C20P. 'Concrete mixes for general purposes', Table C, includes volume batching of C20P.

Fine aggregate is subject to 'bulking' when damp.

~~530~~ ORDINARY PRESCRIBED MIXES to BS 5328, of medium workability, made from:
- Graded coarse aggregate with a nominal maximum size of 20 mm,
- Fine aggregate to BS 882, grading limit M,
may be batched by weight to Table A or Table B of Cement and Concrete Association Publication 45.031 'Concrete mixes for general purposes' 1977.
If batching by volume is permitted (Grades C7.5P, C10P and C15P only) and preferred, it must be to Table C or C&CA Publication 45.031, assuming fine aggregate to be damp at time of batching.

531

BS 5328, Table 2 refers to fine aggregate 'grading zones' as defined in BS 882:1973. The latter has now been withdrawn and replaced by BS 882:1983, Table 5 of which gives 'grading limits'.

The ranges of fine aggregate percentages given here are based on a draft revision to BS 5328. 14 mm aggregate is not normally available and has therefore been excluded.

BS 8110, clause 6.1.3.4 states: 'Standard mixes using fine aggregate gradings Type F are not recommended'. Where the concrete supplier can show that such material can be used to produce satisfactory concrete, approval may be given.

~~531~~ ORDINARY PRESCRIBED MIXES: Table 2 and Notes 2 and 4 of BS 5328 shall not apply. The percentage by mass of fine aggregate to total aggregate to be as follows:

	BS 882 grading limits	Nominal maximum size of aggregate		
		40 mm	20 mm	10 mm
Grades C7.5P C10P and C15P	C, M or F	30-45	35-50	Not applicable
Grades C20P,	C	30-40	35-45	45-55
C25P and C30P	M	25-35	30-40	40-50
	F	25-30	25-35	35-45

In each case a range of fine aggregate percentages is given; the lower percentage is applicable to finer materials and the higher percentage to coarser mater? in each case within the stated BS 882 grading limi? not use BS 882 grading limit F fine aggregate w? approval.

For grades C20P, C25P and C30P, and wh? workability is required, check that the ? fine aggregate stated will produce sati? if the grading of the fine aggregate? coarser limits of grading zone C o? grading zone F.

(550) WATER CONTENT of concre? and adjusted to allow for ? give consistent quality a?

590

Admixtures based on calcium chloride should not be used. See C&CA 'Man on the job' leaflet 45.104 'Concrete admixtures'.

(590) ADMIXTURES: use ? strictly to manufac? and in consultat? proportions i? and harden?

Page 11

A straight-forward choice of clauses according to relevance. The decision to specify designed mixes obtained from a QSRMC accredited plant means that clauses 530 and 531 are not needed. The remaining three pages of the section can be completed with similar ease.

These example pages give an excellent illustration of how the NBS specification writer's time is spent. Depending on his current technical knowledge he will need to read the general guidance notes (pages 1 to 6) and key industry documents. He will then need to decide on and specify the types of concrete mix (pages 7 to 9) and this may take a significant amount of time. The remaining clauses, comprising about 85% of the finished job specification section, can be selected and completed within just a few minutes.

National Engineering Specification

NES is structured in accordance with CAWS for the groups relevant to building services engineering, including:

A   Sub-contract Preliminaries/General conditions
C   Demolition/Alteration/Maintenance
N   Furniture/Equipment
R   Disposal systems
S   Piped supply systems
T   Mechanical heating/Cooling/Refrigeration systems
U   Ventilation/Air conditioning systems
V   Electrical supply/power/lighting systems
W   Communications/Security/Control systems
X   Transport systems
Y   Services reference specifications

The text has the following features:
- All contractual items have been confined to the Preliminaries.
- Materials and workmanship have been separated and workmanship clauses always follow the materials clauses.
- For flexibility in use, many options have been included in the clauses.
- Guidance notes are included alongside the clauses – they are not intended to be a 'design manual', but generally indicate relevant sources of design information.

Project specifications

The structure of NES implies that a derived job specification will have three sections:

1. PRELIMINARIES – The contractual or sub-contractual aspects of the project.

2. SYSTEM SPECIFICATIONS – These are sub-divided into four parts:

   Part 1
   System objectives – clauses giving design information, system performance and system description, together with a list of the system schematics and drawings.
   Part 2
   Selection schedules giving the selected options from the reference specifications (see below) and including equipment duties, etc.
   Part 3
   Specification clauses specific to the system and not covered by the reference specifications.
   Part 4
   Selection schedules giving the selected options from the clauses specific to the system and including equipment duties, etc.

3. REFERENCE SPECIFICATIONS (Clauses from the Y group) – This contains all the reference specifications relevant to all the systems for the project. Options are selected in Part 2 of the System specifications.

Example project specification

The following pages show part of a typical project specification and are taken from NES work section T31 and NES reference specification Y10.

T31 LOW TEMPERATURE HOT WATER HEATING

1000   SYSTEM OBJECTIVES

1010   PERFORMANCE OBJECTIVES
The conference centre committee rooms and circulation areas will be heated by a LTHW heating system.

1030   SYSTEM DESCRIPTION
The LTHW heating system will consist of radiators installed in the committee rooms and in staircases as shown on the drawings to maintain the space temperature.

PART 2 SELECTION SCHEDULES FOR REFERENCE SPECIFICATIONS

2100   PIPELINES

2101   PIPELINES GENERALLY: Comply with Work Section Y10 General clauses and those detailed below.

21051 PIPES AND FITTINGS: Type 1
        Application
        Pipework up to and including 50mm

        Pipes - reference Y10.2010
          Dimensions Heavy
          Ends   Screwed
          Finish   Varnished
        Fittings - reference Y10.2070
          Finish   Black
        Jointing   Screwed
        Jointing materials
          Screwed joints to BS 21 - reference Y10.3030
            Use hemp and jointing compound to BS 5292
            Unions connections - reference Y10.3040
              Seating
                bronze to iron, railroad pattern

21052 PIPES AND FITTINGS: Type 2
        Application
        Pipework above 50 mm

        Pipes - reference Y10.2010
          Dimensions Heavy
          Ends   Plain
          Finish   Varnished
        Fittings - reference Y10.2060
          Material   Carbon steel grade 410 electric
                      resistance welded
          Ends   Plain
          Finish   Varnished
        Jointing   Welded
        Jointing materials
          Flanges - reference Y10.3010
            BS 4504 PN 16
            Material
              Mild steel
            Face
              slip on type for welding
          Joint rings - Reference Y10.3020
            Type
              Full face
            Material
              Corrugated copper nickel alloy to BS
              5292
        Welding
          Rods - reference Y10.3050
            Steel pipes, use rods
              Gas welding, BS 1453 type A2 or A3
            or Electric arc welding BS 2633

123

2109 WORKMANSHIP:
    Appearance - reference Y10.4010
    Spacing - reference Y10.4020
    Pipework gradients - reference Y10.4030
       Install pipework to the falls shown on drawings
    Air vent requirements - reference Y10.4040
       An air bottle - a vertical extension from the pipe approximately 100mm long, at the bore of the pipe, with a copper extension pipe with a manual vent cock located in an easily accessible position.
    Drain requirements - reference Y10.4050
    Expansion and contraction - reference Y10.4060
    Pipe fittings - reference Y10.4070
       Use elbows and square tees.
    Pipes through walls and floors - reference Y10.4110
    Pipe sleeves - reference Y10.4120
    Wall and floor masking plates - reference Y10.4130
    Connections to equipment - reference Y10.4140
    Temporary plugs, caps and flanges
       Reference Y10.4160
    Welding general - reference Y10.4170
       Welded joints Class 2
       Radiographic examination of welds not required
    Welded joints, steel pipes - reference Y10.4180
    Painting welded joints, steel pipes
       Reference Y10.4185
    Flanged joints general - reference Y10.4200
    Flanged joints, steel pipes - reference Y10.4210
    Screwed joints, steel pipes - reference Y10.4220
    Dissimilar metals - reference Y10.4320
    Pipe rings and clips - reference Y10.4330
    Pipe supports - reference Y10.4360
    Support spacing - reference Y10.4370
    Isolation and regulation - reference Y10.4380
       Provide isolation and regulation valves
          where shown on drawings

PART 3 SPECIFICATION CLAUSES SPECIFIC TO T31
    Clauses marked with a * are options. Selection of required options are made in Part 4 - Selection Schedules for Specification clauses specific to T31.

3000 GENERAL

3010 SITE DIMENSIONS: Check prior to ordering.

3020 TESTING: Test at manufacturer's works to appropriate British Standard to suit pressure and temperature conditions of system.

4000 PRODUCTS/MATERIALS

4010 RADIATORS GENERALLY: Ensure radiators are manufactured and rated in accordance with BS 3528.

4020 RADIATORS - STEEL PANEL:
Type   * Welded top type
           * Round top type
           * Single panel
           * Double panel
           * Vertical style
           * Horizontal style
           * Convector type
           * Low temperature type
           * Special shape as indicated
Connections: Wrought iron bosses welded on at manufacturer's works.
Air cock : Provide return end air cock recessed within unit length.
Finish   * Degrease and protect against rusting before application of a high quality stove primer.
           * Stove enamelled, colour as indicated
Testing : Test to BS 3528, not less than 7 bar (gauge) or one and a half times maximum working pressure whichever is greater.
Accessories
           * Welded feet and top stay
           * Wall brackets

5000 WORKMANSHIP

5010 INSTALLATION: Install in accordance with manufacturer's recommendations to give a neat appearance, with supports out of view where possible. Ensure equipment is firmly fixed and level.

5020 BUILDERSWORK: Mark out positions for battens fixed by others, when fixing equipment to stud walling.

5030 ISOLATION: Fit an isolating valve on flow and a regulating valve on return unless otherwise indicated.

PART 4 SELECTION SCHEDULES FOR CLAUSES SPECIFIC TO T31

6000 LOW PRESSURE HOT WATER SYSTEM SELECTION SCHEDULE

6010 HEATING EQUIPMENT SCHEDULES: Supply heating equipment as:-

  schedule numbers 1234

6020 GENERAL
  Site dimensions - reference T31.3010
  Testing - reference T31.3020

6030 RADIATORS:
  Radiators generally - reference T31.4010
  Steel panel - reference T31.4020

  Application
    Radiators installed throughout building as detailed in schedule in positions shown on drawing

Number required	As schedule
Output	As schedule
Mean water temperature	As schedule
Room air temperature	As schedule
Water flow rate	As schedule

  Steel panel
    Size

Sections	As schedule
Height	As schedule

    Type
      Round top type
      Single panel
    Finish
      Degrease and protect against rusting before application of a high quality stove primer.
    Accessories
      Wall brackets

6120 WORKMANSHIP
  Installation - reference T31.5010
  Builders work - reference T31.5020
  Isolation - reference T31.5030

Y10 PIPELINES

OPTIONS

Clauses marked with a * are options. Selection of required options is made in Work Section Selection Schedules for Reference Specifications.

1000 GENERAL

1010 PRE-FABRICATED PIPEWORK: Supply pre-fabricated pipework in accordance with relevant materials and worksmanship clauses.

1020 FITTINGS: For changes in direction use centreline radius/nominal bore of not less than 1.5 unless otherwise directed. For reductions and enlargements use easy transition type with inclined angle not exceeding 30 degrees.

1030 FABRICATED FITTINGS: Use only with approval, if manufacturer's standard fittings are not available.

1040 PIPE JOINTS: Obtain approval from Local Water Authority or National Water Council for materials used in water supplies.

2000 PRODUCTS/MATERIALS PIPELINES

2010 CARBON STEEL TO BS 1387
```
Material    : Carbon steel
Standard    : BS 1387
Dimensions  * Light
            * Medium
            * Heavy
            : Random single lengths, 4m to 7m
Ends        * Screwed to BS 21, taper thread
            * Plain
Finish      * Unvarnished
            * Varnished
            * Galvanized
```

2020 CARBON STEEL FITTINGS, SCREWED BENDS AND SPRINGS TO BS 1387

```
Material    * Carbon steel grade, seamless
            * Carbon steel grade, welded
Standard    : BS 1387
Size range  : 6mm to 150mm
Dimensions  : BS 1387 - minimum weight
Ends        : Screwed to BS 21

Finish      * Unvarnished
            * Varnished
            * Galvanized
```

2070 MALLEABLE CAST IRON FITTINGS, SCREWED TO BS 143 AND 1256
```
Material    : Malleable cast iron, grade W22/4 to BS
              309 or grade B18/6 to BS 310.
Standard    : BS 143 or 1256
Size range  : 10mm to 164mm
Dimensions  : BS 143 or 1256
Ends        : Screwed to BS 143 or 1256
Finish      * Unvarnished
            * Varnished
            * Galvanized
```

3000 PRODUCTS/MATERIALS - JOINTING MATERIALS

3010 FLANGES TO BS 4504 PART 1 AND PART 2: Select flanges from the appropriate table and supply:-
```
            * Mild steel
            * Copper Alloy flanges - High tensile brass
            * Composite flanges
Flange type * Flat face for screwed fixing
            * Raised face for screwed fixing
            * Slip on type for welding
            * Welding neck type for welding
```

Associated bolts, nuts and washers.
: For ferrous and composite flanges:-
: Interior use - Black mild steel
: Exterior use - Cadmium plated to BS 3382 Part 1
: For copper alloy flanges use high tensile brass

3020 FLANGE JOINTING RINGS: Use flange jointing rings to suit face type, as indicated.
* Full face
* Within bolt circle

Supply joint rings manufactured from:-
* Compressed asbestos fibre to BS 2815 and 1832,
* High grade natural rubber to BS 2494,
* Corrugated copper nickel alloy to BS 5292

3030 SCREWED JOINTS TO BS 21:
* Use hemp and jointing compound to BS 5292
* Use PTFE tape to BS 4375

4000 WORKMANSHIP

4010 APPEARANCE: Arrange all exposed pipe runs to present neat appearance, parallel with other pipe or service runs and building structure, subject to gradients for draining or venting.
Ensure all vertical pipes are plumb or follow building line.

4020 SPACING: Space pipe runs in relation to one another, other services runs and building structure, allow for specified thickness of thermal insulation and ensure adequate space for access to pipe joints, etc.
The following are recommended as minimum clearances in spacing of pipe runs:-

BETWEEN	AND	CLEARANCE - mm
pipeline -	wall finish	25
insulated or	ceiling finish	
uninsulated	or soffit	50
	floor finish	150
insulated	adjacent service	
pipeline	runs	25
uninsulated	adjacent service	
pipeline	runs	50
adjacent	both uninsulated	150
pipelines	one insulated -	
	one uninsulated	75
	both insulated	25

4030 GRADIENTS: Install pipework with gradients to allow drainage and/or air release, and to the slopes where indicated.

4040 AIR VENT REQUIREMENTS: Air Vent Assembly
* An air bottle - a vertical extension from the pipe approximately 100mm long, at the bore of the pipe.
* An air bottle - a vertical extension from the pipe approximately 100mm long, at the bore of the pipe, with a copper extension pipe with a manual vent cock located in an easily accessible position.
* An automatic air vent valve.
* An automatic air vent valve, with a copper outlet pipe from the valve to a tundish in an adjacent drain line or to another suitable location.

4050 DRAIN REQUIREMENTS: Grade pipework to allow system to be drained.

4060 EXPANSION AND CONTRACTION: Arrange supports and fixings to accommodate pipe movement caused by the thermal changes, generally allow the flexure at changes in direction. Allow for movement at branch connections.

4110 PIPES THROUGH WALLS AND FLOORS: Enclose pipes passing through building elements, (walls, floors, partitions, etc.) concentrically within purpose made sleeves. Fit masking plates where visible pipes pass through building elements, including false ceilings of occupied rooms.

4120 PIPE SLEEVES: Cut sleeves from material same as pipe one or two sizes larger than pipe, or pipe and insulation if insulation is carried through sleeve, to allow clearance. Do not use sleeves as pipe supports. Install sleeves flush with building finish. In areas where floors are washed down install with a 100mm protrusion above floor finish.
Pack annular space between pipe and sleeve with mineral wool or similar non-flammable and fire resistant material to form a fire/smoke stop of required rating. Apply 12mm deep cold mastic seal at both ends within sleeve.

4130 WALL, FLOOR AND CEILING MASKING PLATES:
Material   : Copper alloy, chromium plated
Type   : Heavy, split on the diameter, close fitting to the outside wall of the pipe.
Fixing   : Chrome raised head fixing screws

4140 CONNECTIONS TO EQUIPMENT: Make final connections to equipment in accordance with manufacturer's instructions and as indicated.

4160 TEMPORARY PLUGS, CAPS AND FLANGES: Seal all open ends as installation proceeds by metal, plastic or wooden plugs, caps or blank flanges, to prevent ingress of foreign matter.
In the event of such precautions not being taken, order pipework adjacent to open ends to be stripped out to such a point or points that will demonstrate that fouling of bores has not occurred.

4170 WELDING GENERAL: Use skilled craftsman in possession of a current Certificate of Competence appropriate to type and class of work, issued by an approved authority. Mark each weld to identify operative. Submit specimen welds, representative of joints and conditions of site welding, for each craftsman, test non-destructively, approximately 10% of buttweld joints and 5% of all other joints.
* Welded Joints Class 1 - Weld pipeline joints to BS 1821 and BS 2633 as appropriate. Carry out non-destructive testing on 10% or as indicated.
* Welded Joints Class 2 - Weld pipeline joints to BS 2640 and BS 2971 and to HVCA Code of Practice TR/5, Welding of Carbon Steel Pipework, as appropriate.
* Examine welds radiographically, percentage as indicated.

4180 WELDED JOINTS, STEEL PIPES: Preparation, Making and Sealing
: Oxy-acetylene welding, conforming to BS 1821 or BS 2640 appropriate to system temperature and pressure.
: Arc welding, conforming to BS 2633 or BS 2971 appropriate to system temperature and pressure. Use arc welding process on piping greater than 100mm.

4185 PAINTING WELDED JOINTS, STEEL PIPES: Unless pipework is being prepared for galvanizing after manufacture, wire brush and paint all welds with red oxide paint when welds are complete.

4200 FLANGED JOINTS GENERAL: Use number and diameters of bolts to standard. Fit bolts of length to give not less than one thread, or more than 3mm protrusion beyond nut when joint is pulled up.
Fit washers under each hexagonal bolt head and nut.

4210 FLANGED JOINTS, STEEL PIPES:
Welded
Flanges   : Weld neck and bore of 'slip on' flange.
            : Butt weld neck of welding neck flange.
Screwed
Flanges   : Apply jointing materials. Screw on flange
              and expand tube into flange with roller
              expander where necessary.
Preparation: Ensure that flange mating faces are
              parallel; flange peripheries are flush
              with each other; and bolt holes are
              correctly aligned.
Making and
Sealing   : Insert jointing between flange mating
              faces. Pull up joint equally all round.

4220 SCREWED JOINTS, STEEL PIPES:
Preparation: Ensure that plain ends are cut square.
              Reamer out bore at plain ends. Screw
              plain ends, taper thread.
Making and
Sealing   : Coat male pipe threads with jointing
              compound and hemp, or PTFE tape on small
              sizes. Immediately after applying
              coating, connect with female end of
              socket or fitting, and tighten ensuring
              that coating does not intrude into pipe.
              Leave joint clean.

4320 DISSIMILAR METALS: Take appropriate means to prevent galvanic action where dissimilar metals are connected together.

4330 PIPE RINGS AND CLIPS: Select type according to the application and material compatibility, give particular attention where pipes are subject to axial movement due to expansion or contraction.
Use pipe clips as BS 3974 Part 1, take into account the pipe load, material and pipe/insulation surface temperature.

4360 PIPE SUPPORTS: Arrange supports and accessories for equipment, appliances or ancillary fitments in pipe runs, so that no undue strain is imposed upon pipes. Ensure that materials used for supports are compatible with pipeline materials.

4390 MAINTENANCE AND RENEWAL: Arrange pipework, valves, drains, air vents, demountable joints, supports, etc., for convenient routine maintenance and renewals. Provide all runs with a regularly spaced pattern of demountable joints in the form of unions, flanges, etc., and also at items of equipment to facilitate disconnection.
Locate valves, drains, flanges etc. in groups.

4450 CLEANING: Remove cement and clean off all pipework and brackets.

4460 STEEL PIPEWORK PAINTING: Remove scale, rust or temporary protective coating by chipping, wire brushing or use of approved solvents and paint with one coat of red oxide primer, as work proceeds.

4470 STEELWORK PAINTING: Prepare supports, bearers and other uncovered steelwork as steel pipework. Where not exposed, paint with one coat zinc chromate or red oxide primer.

Appendix 1

Members of the Specification Working Group and Consultant

ACE Representatives

Paul Hansen, MSc, MIngF
Bill Howard-Jones, CEng, MIMechE, FIPetE, MBIH
John James, FCIBS, MConsE
Gordon Vincent, MSc, CEng, FIMechE, FIEE, FCIBS, MConsE

BEC Representatives

Peter Jordan, CEng, MICE, FCIOB (Secretary)
Leaster Crossley
Edward Turton, ARICS

RIBA Representatives

Paul Castle, BArch, RIBA (Chairman)
John Gammans, AADip, DipTD
Douglas Smith, DipArch, FRIBA, FLI
Professor Douglass Wise, OBE, BArch, DipTP, RIBA

RICS Representatives

Malcolm Boyd, FRICS
Brian Edgill, FRICS
Michael Whatford, ARICS (until March 1983)

Consultant

Tony Allott, BArch, FRIBA (National Building Specification Ltd).